**INDEPENDENT COFFEE GUIDE
ENGLAND: NORTH, MIDLANDS & EAST NO 7
IS SUPPORTED BY**

Organic ACORN DAIRY

CAKESMITHS
CAKES FOR COFFEE SHOPS

CUP NORTH

Harry's
Artisan Hot Chocolate
& Bakery

HUNDRED
HOUSE COFFEE

NOTTINGHAM
COFFEE
FESTIVAL

salt

Zettle
by PayPal

FOR BREW FREAKS, BEAN GEEKS

AND THE SIMPLY CURIOUS ...

Independent Coffee Guide team:

Richard Bailey, Nick Cooper, Charlotte Cummins, Kathryn Lewis, Abi Manning, Melissa Morris, Tamsin Powell, Jo Rees, Rosanna Rothery, Ben Sibley, Melissa Stewart, Mark Tibbles and Selena Young.

A big thank you to the Independent Coffee Guide committee (meet them on page 200) for their expertise and enthusiasm, and to our sponsors Acorn Dairy, Birmingham Coffee Festival, Cakesmiths, Harry's Hot Chocolate, Hundred House Coffee, Manchester Coffee Festival, Nottingham Coffee Festival and Zettle.

Coffee shops, cafes and roasteries are invited to be included in the guide based on meeting criteria set by the committee, which includes the use of speciality beans, providing a high-quality coffee experience for visitors and being independently run.

For information on Independent Coffee Guides for Ireland, Scotland, South England, and Wales, visit:

INDYCOFFEE.GUIDE

indycoffeeguide

© Salt Media Ltd

Published by Salt Media Ltd 2023

saltmedia.co.uk

01271 859299

ideas@saltmedia.co.uk

CONTENTS

Page

WELCOME

I'm stoked to introduce the newly extended *England: North, Midlands and East* edition of the *Indy Coffee Guide*. We've expanded further across England to include Norfolk, Suffolk and Cambridgeshire and given the guide a fresh look to reflect the ever-changing speciality scene.

It's always exciting to explore another coffee region and we're thrilled to share some very special finds with you. From a roaming crew of first-responders-turned-baristas to an espresso bar hidden in a houseplant shop and a roastery in a 500-year-old barn, unique speciality experiences await.

Observant coffee fans will notice that North Wales is missing from this edition. Don't panic: we have a dedicated Wales guide in the pipeline for autumn 2023, ready to fuel your caffeinated adventures across Cymru.

As always, we love to see where the guide takes you so do share your experiences with us on Instagram. And if there's a cafe or roastery you think deserves to be in the next edition, drop us a message.

Enjoy.

Kathryn Lewis

Editor
Indy Coffee Guides
🄾 *indycoffeeguide*

HOW TO USE THE GUIDE

CAFES

Coffee shops and cafes where you can drink top-notch speciality coffee. We've split the guide into areas to help you find places near you.

ROASTERIES

Meet the leading speciality coffee roasters and discover where to source beans. Find them after the cafes in each area.

MAPS

Every cafe and roastery has a number so you can find them either on the area map at the start of each section or on the detailed city maps.

MORE GOOD STUFF

Discover **more good cups** and **more good roasteries** at the back of the book.

Follow us on Instagram:
 indycoffeeguide

YOUR ADVENTURES START HERE

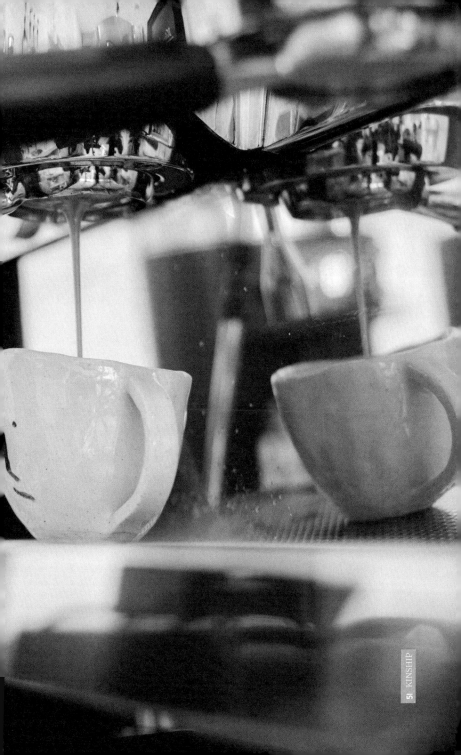

TYNE AND WEAR & COUNTY DURHAM

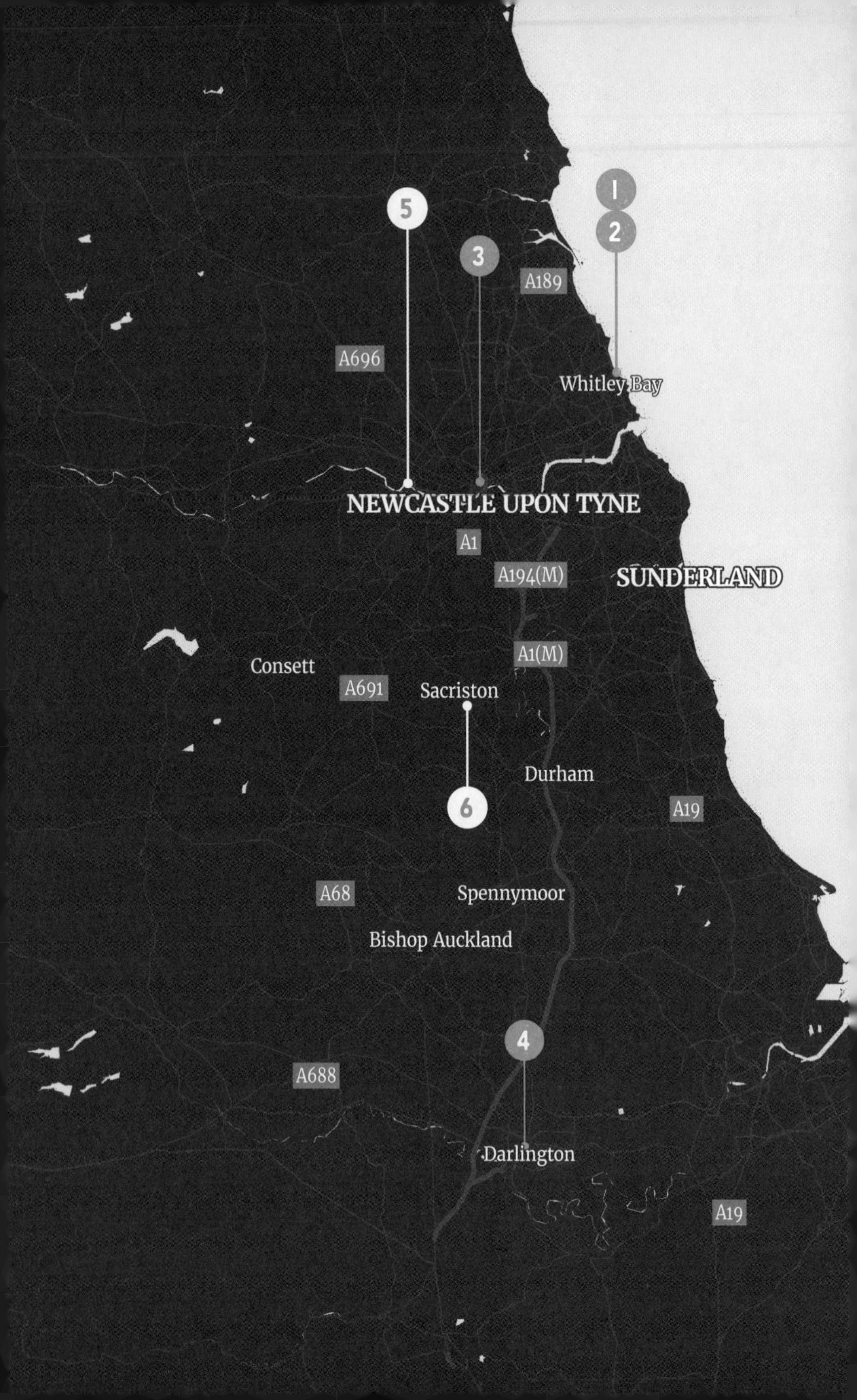
1
2
5
3
A189
A696
Whitley Bay
NEWCASTLE UPON TYNE
A1
A194(M)
SUNDERLAND
A1(M)
Consett
A691
Sacriston
Durham
6
A19
A68
Spennymoor
Bishop Auckland
4
A688
Darlington
A19

CAFES

1 PureKnead – Whitley Bay
2 Rustic Cup
3 PureKnead – Newcastle
4 Hatch Luncheonette

ROASTERIES

5 Gold Box Roastery
6 Durham Coffee

Find more good cafes and roasteries on pages 192-199

***All locations are approximate**

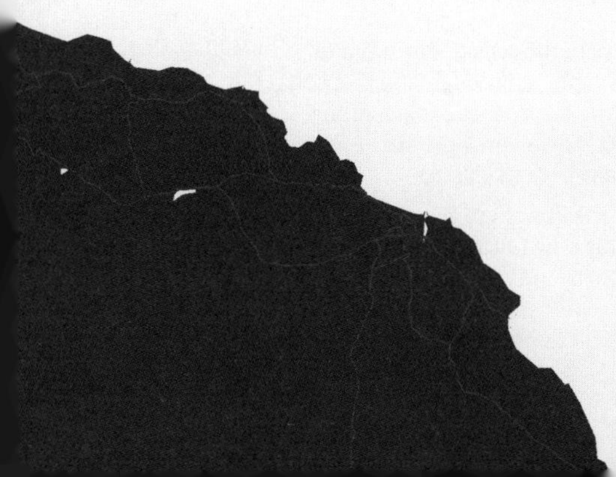

I PUREKNEAD - WHITLEY BAY

111-113 Park View, Whitley Bay, Tyne and Wear, NE26 3RH

pure-knead.co.uk | 07964 864181

f *purekneadwhitleybay* *ⓘ* *purekneadbakery*

Baking may be fundamentally scientific, but cast your eye over the cakes and pastries adorning the PureKnead counter and you'd think their creator was a trained artist ... and you'd be right.

In 2015, returning to work after the birth of her children, fine-art graduate Paula Watson committed to putting her degree to gastronomic use. She started with a cake stall at Tynemouth Market and, after 18 months of successful trading, moved the flourishing business to a vacant shop in Whitley Bay.

TIP TREAT YOURSELF TO A SLICE OF THE GRAVITY-DEFYING LEMON MERINGUE PIE

Seven years on, PureKnead is famous in the seaside town – and beyond – for its cinnamon buns, 48-hour sourdough and bespoke custom bakes. While the ingredients used are local, much of the inspiration is international. Regulars queue down the street for Copenhagen-inspired pastries and antipodean classics.

Coffee drinkers can be assured that the brews are as good as the bakes: the house coffee is Square Mile's Red Brick blend and a bank of excellent baristas deliver consistently silky pours.

Established
2016

Key roaster
Square Mile
Coffee Roasters

Brewing method
Espresso, V60

Machine
Victoria Arduino
White Eagle

Grinder
Mythos One,
Nuova Simonelli
MDJ, Fellow ODE

Opening hours
Tue–Sun
10am–2pm

REUSABLES
ACCEPTED

DOGS
WELCOME

BUY BEANS
IN STORE

COFFEE
COURSES

WHITLEY BAY

22

2 RUSTIC CUP

28 Park View, Whitley Bay, Tyne and Wear, NE26 2TH

rusticcup.co.uk | 07935 096539

f *rusticcup.uk* *⊙* *rusticcup.uk*

Whether you're nipping in to grab beans to brew at home or settling in for a nutritious brunch, you're assured of a warm welcome and a fantastic coffee at Rustic Cup.

Before moving to the North East, Lee Coates and Veronika Pitakova (the globetrotting bikers behind the cafe) explored coffee culture at its source. From growing their own beans in Timor-Leste to mastering brewing techniques in Italy, they got stuck into all areas of the speciality industry before establishing their own venue. The result is a coffee offering bursting with passion and expertise.

TIP CHECK SOCIAL FOR UPCOMING EVENTS

Just like the meticulously prepped Baristocracy brews, Rustic Cup's food is crafted to lift the spirits – from kaleidoscopic smoothie bowls and salads to ciabattas crammed with local produce. Add craft beers, wines and an impressive cocktail list to the mix and an early brunch could easily turn into a rather long lunch.

The team recently expanded the seating capacity of this Whitley Bay community hub, so there's plenty of space to chill out and explore the vast coffee menu.

Established
2020

Key roaster
Baristocracy
Coffee Roasters

Brewing method
Espresso, drip,
batch brew,
Chemex, V60

Machine
La Marzocco
KB90 ABR

Grinder
Mahlkonig E65S
GbW,
Mahlkonig EK43 S,
Mythos One

Opening hours
Mon-Sat
7.30am–5pm
Sun
9am–4pm

REUSABLES ACCEPTED   WIFI   DOGS WELCOME   BUY BEANS IN STORE   OUTDOOR SEATING

3 PUREKNEAD - NEWCASTLE

38 Dean Street, Newcastle, NE1 1PG

pure-knead.co.uk | 01912 305857

f *purekneadwhitleybay* ⦿ *purekneadnewcastle*

Building on the roaring success of the original PureKnead site in Whitley Bay, this Newcastle spin-off was an instant hit when it opened in the heart of the city in October 2021.

Its counter mirrors that of the OG and showcases a lip-smacking daily line-up of breads, bakes and cakes. Fresh and generously filled sandwiches, made with PureKnead's fabulous 48-hour sourdough, are stacked high each morning.

TIP ARRIVE EARLY TO BAG A SLICE OF THE BEST-SELLING SALTED CARAMEL CHOCOLATE TART

London's Square Mile supplies both venues with its crowd-pleasing Red Brick blend for the house espresso, while in Newcastle there's also a new guest-roaster programme which offers a spectrum of single origins from the likes of North Star, Assembly and Outpost.

Want to be as good as the baristas? The team offer one-on-one training sessions to help home brewers polish their skills. You'll be taught the theory of dialling in and how to steam milk before putting it into practice on the shop's Victoria Arduino machine.

Established
2021

Key roaster
Square Mile
Coffee Roasters

Brewing method
Espresso, V60

Machine
Victoria Arduino
Eagle One

Grinder
Mythos One,
Nuova Simonelli
MDJ, Fellow ODE

Opening hours
Tue–Fri
8.30am–4pm
Sat
10am–4pm
Sun
10am–3pm

REUSABLES ACCEPTED   DOGS WELCOME   BUY BEANS IN STORE   COFFEE COURSES

NEWCASTLE

24

4 HATCH LUNCHEONETTE

32 Blackwellgate, Darlington, County Durham, DL1 5HN

01325 380720

f hatchluncheonette   *⊚ hatchluncheonette*

You know you're in for a fantastic flat white when you discover that its beans are roasted just a few miles down the road and the milk is sourced from an organic farm nearby. The Hatch baristas have even paid a visit (or three) to the free-range cows that produce the creamy whole milk, and have close links with the roasters at Rounton who provide the house coffee for Hatch's glossy espresso.

TIP TOO BUSY TO STOP? POP INTO 'HATCH TO GO' NEXT DOOR

While the pro baristas knock out consistently delicious flat whites and filters at the bar of this Scandi-style cafe, owners Jasmin and Phil Robson spend their day in the kitchen where they prepare scrumptious dishes from locally sourced ingredients.

Seasonal specials such as burrata with cherry tomatoes, vegan 'nduja, basil pesto and sourdough are best enjoyed in the upstairs seating area where light pours in and verdant houseplants thrive. On sunny days, Hatch's windows are flung open to create an indoor-outdoor vibe, and the team whip out their Italian Carpigiani machine to serve luscious soft-serve ice cream.

Established
2018

Key roaster
Rounton Coffee Roasters

Brewing method
Espresso, filter

Machine
Sanremo Café Racer

Grinder
Fiorenzato F64

Opening hours
Wed–Sat
9am–5pm
Sun
10am–4pm

DARLINGTON

REUSABLES ACCEPTED

BIKE FRIENDLY

DOGS WELCOME

BUY BEANS IN STORE

OUTDOOR SEATING

TYNE AND WEAR & COUNTY DURHAM
ROASTERIES

5 GOLD BOX ROASTERY

6–8 Vance Court, Blaydon, Tyne and Wear, NE21 5NH

goldboxroastery.com | 07788 427423

f *goldboxroastery* ⊚ *goldboxroastery*

The team at Gold Box are on a mission to caffeinate the globe. Between their original roastery in Newcastle and an outpost in Dubai, they're providing beans for a world of wholesale and retail customers.

From their HQ in Blaydon, the Gold Box roasters (which include a Q grader and a Brewers Cup championship barista) specialise in crafting unique coffees and sourcing rare and interesting beans. Each sip is the pinnacle of a journey that's taken the team up mountains and through rainforests to procure beans that tick the boxes for altitude, soil quality, farming techniques, community welfare and sustainability.

Barbara Croce, founder of the eco-focused business (it's marching towards the goal of becoming plastic-free) says: *'Great-tasting coffee begins with the best beans, but it's the art of roasting that's essential to producing the perfect cup.'*

'TICK THE BOXES FOR ALTITUDE, SOIL QUALITY, FARMING TECHNIQUES, COMMUNITY WELFARE AND SUSTAINABILITY'

Gold Box's multiple awards and accolades, which include sourcing and roasting the winning coffee for Michaela Ruazol in the 2022 World Coffee Championships, are testament to this approach.

Established
2013

Roaster make and size
Probat P25 25kg,
Probat P12 12kg,
HB-L2 2kg,
Aillio Bullet 1kg,
HB-M6 600g

COFFEE COURSES

BUY BEANS ONLINE

BUY BEANS IN STORE

6 DURHAM COFFEE

AMR Building, Sacriston Industrial Estate, Plawsworth Road, Sacriston, Durham, DH7 6JX

durhamcoffee.co.uk | 01914 474552

f *durhamcoffeeuk* ⊙ *durhamcoffeeuk*

Want to improve your home brews, become a super-slick barista or master the art of roasting? This roastery and training space is where novices in the North East head to learn the tricks of the trade before graduating equipped with the skills to serve (and even roast) cafe-quality coffee.

Father-and-daughter founders Bernhard and Carina Nausner love to share their enthusiasm, experience and knowledge with like-minded coffee folk, whether through hands-on courses or simply over a cup of the good stuff at their roastery.

'BERNHARD AND CARINA LOVE TO SHARE THEIR ENTHUSIASM, EXPERIENCE AND KNOWLEDGE'

When they're not teaching, Bernhard and Carina roast sustainably sourced green beans in a duo of Air-Motion roasters, using an IKAWA Pro for sampling. Their core range is made up of two espresso blends and single origins from Brazil, Ethiopia, India, Colombia, Guatemala and Uganda.

Those making a trip to the roastery should ask what's new, as the pair release four or five limited-edition coffees each year which are worth hunting out. Previous hits include a punchy Peruvian and a sought-after El Salvadoran.

Established
2020

Roaster make and size
Air-Motion 12kg,
Air-Motion 3kg,
IKAWA Pro V3

COFFEE COURSES

BUY BEANS ONLINE

BUY BEANS IN STORE

CUMBRIA,
LANCASHIRE &
MERSEYSIDE

CAFES

7 Fold Coffee
8 Marra
9 Atkinsons The Castle
10 Atkinsons The Hall
11 Atkinsons The Music Room
12 Journey Social Kitchen
13 Rise - Preston
14 Four One Two
15 Bloom & Brew

ROASTERIES

24 Rinaldo's Speciality Coffee & Fine Tea
25 Carringtons Coffee Co.
26 Atkinsons Coffee Roasters

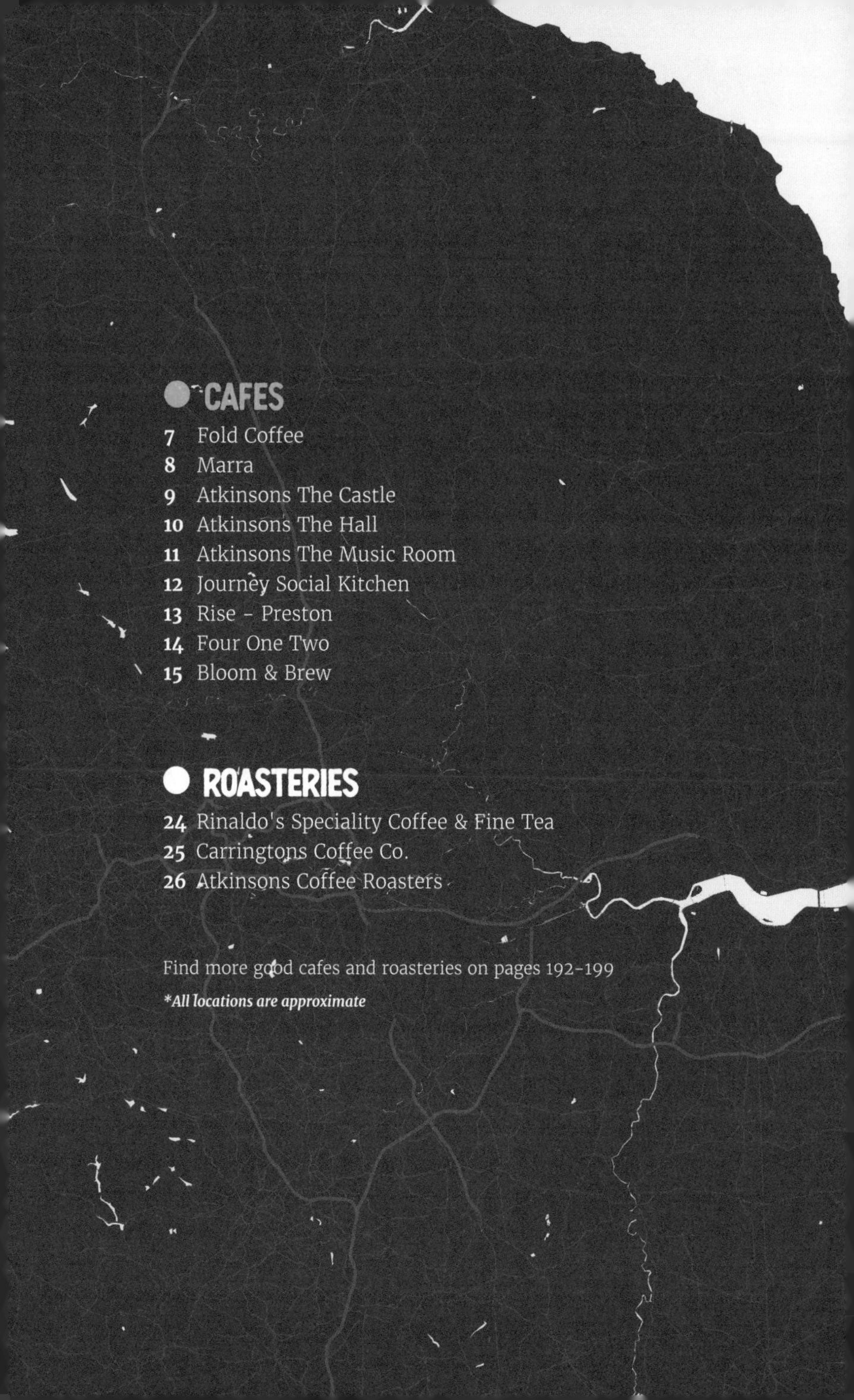

Find more good cafes and roasteries on pages 192-199

**All locations are approximate*

LIVERPOOL

● CAFES

● ROASTERIES

Find more good cafes and roasteries on pages 192–199

All locations are approximate

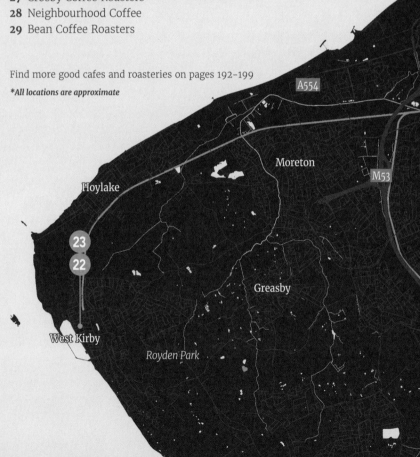

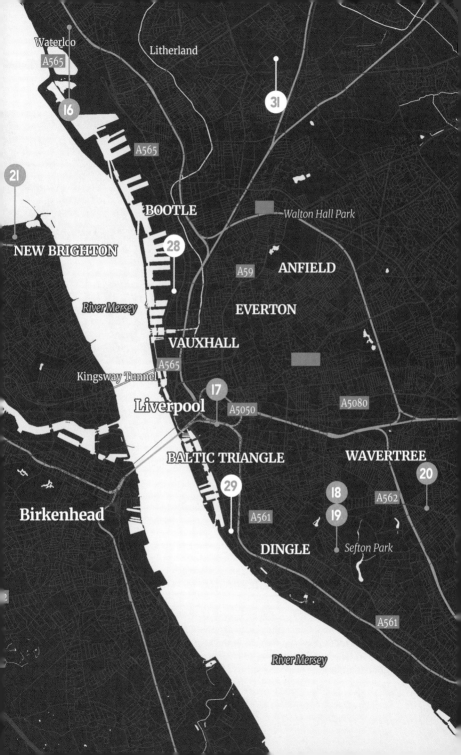

Waterloo

A565

16

Litherland

31

21

BOOTLE

A565

28

NEW BRIGHTON

River Mersey

Walton Hall Park

A59

ANFIELD

EVERTON

VAUXHALL

A565

Kingsway Tunnel

Liverpool

17

A5050

A5080

BALTIC TRIANGLE

WAVERTREE

29

20

18

A562

Birkenhead

A561

19

DINGLE

Sefton Park

River Mersey

A561

7 FOLD COFFEE

Unit 12 Beezon Road Industrial Estate, Kendal, Cumbria, LA9 6BW

07587 525829

f foldbyfell *foldbyfell*

Since opening this Kendal coffee shop in 2021, Jack and Chelsea Eddy-Waland have created a welcoming space where everything, right down to the coffee cups, is crafted in Cumbria.

A wood burner, sofa and fully stocked bookshelf make it a cosy destination to shelter from the elements. The early-morning opening hours, however, ensure that savouries, cakes and coffee to-go are equally as popular with outdoor adventurers fuelling a trek through the fells.

TIP A LINE-UP OF LIVE MUSIC AND ARTISAN WORKSHOPS ADDS TO THE FUN VIBE

Ramblers and relaxers alike relish a cup of Onwards, an espresso roasted in Kendal by Red Bank. More complex than your average house blend, it changes with the seasons and is delicious paired with Scandi-style pastries, cakes, bagels and rugbrød (Danish rye bread). An under-the-counter Modbar ensures each shot of coffee is pulled with style, consistency and a touch of theatre.

There's always small-batch filter on the go too, plus a food menu that includes croissants oozing with cheese and roasted ham, and banana bread lavished with blueberry compote and brûléed mascarpone.

Established
2021

Key roaster
Red Bank
Coffee Roasters

Brewing method
Espresso, filter

Machine
La Marzocco
Modbar AV

Grinder
Mahlkonig EK43 S,
Mahlkonig E65S

Opening hours
Mon–Fri
7.30am–2.30pm
Sat–Sun
8.30am–2.30pm

REUSABLES ACCEPTED

WIFI

BIKE FRIENDLY

DOGS WELCOME

OUTDOOR SEATING

8 MARRA

46 Branthwaite Brow, Kendal, Cumbria, LA9 4TX

marra46.co.uk | 07585 320522

Marra Kendal *marra46_kendal*

Before he opened this cosy nook in the heart of Kendal, Marra founder James Tucker ran Yard 46, a popular cafe famed for its homemade small-batch sourdough. His next project was a street food van which, following a win at the Cumbria Food Awards 2022, evolved into this bricks-and-mortar cafe and restaurant.

To find Marra's historic home from Branthwaite Brow, follow the swing sign down a narrow alley to a cobbled courtyard. Inside, blackened beams (rumoured to be from tall ships docked in Cumbria), an open fireplace and period features make it an incredibly snug spot in which to hunker down.

TIP ALREADY EATEN? PICK UP A GOLDEN-TOPPED PASTEL DE NATA FOR LATER

Huddersfield roastery Dark Woods supplies the coffee, its Under Milk Wood blend (notes of caramel, praline and stewed fruits) used for espresso while Good Morning Sunshine (stone fruits, cocoa and cinder toffee flavours) delivers on batch brew. A guest filter spot is reserved for regional roasteries and features the likes of local newbie Podda & Wren.

If you're out and about on a coffee tour, bookmark Marra for a lunch stop. The star of the show is the piadina (a traditional Italian flatbread sandwich), but you'll also find sourdough pizza and bruschetta on the menu.

Established
2022

Key roaster
Dark Woods Coffee

Brewing method
Espresso, filter

Machine
Conti CC202

Grinder
Compak E6,
Bunn FPG,
HeyCafe H1

Opening hours
Mon–Sat
10am–3pm

WIFI | DOGS WELCOME | OUTDOOR SEATING

9 ATKINSONS THE CASTLE

Lancaster Castle, Castle Hill, Lancaster, Lancashire, LA1 1YN

thecoffeehopper.com | 01524 65470

f lancastercastlecafe ⊙ *atkinsons.coffee*

Generally, tourist attractions don't have a great reputation for serving quality coffee, yet the recently restored Lancaster Castle bucks the trend and draws crowds for both its Norman architecture and single-origin espresso.

Overlooking the city for almost 1,000 years, the castle was a fully functioning prison until 2011. In 2019, after extensive renovation, it was opened to the public and the cafe in the grounds entrusted to local speciality legends Atkinsons Coffee Roasters.

TIP DON'T LEAVE TOWN WITHOUT VISITING SISTER VENUES THE HALL AND THE MUSIC ROOM

The contemporary cafe space is kitted out with birch plywood, metro tiles and minimalist houseplants, creating a modern counterpart to the historic setting. Take a seat on the piazza to enjoy an own-roasted flat white and freshly baked pastry while admiring the newly uncovered cloisters and restored turrets.

All the coffee beans, loose-leaf teas and baked goods are delivered daily from the Atkinsons roastery and bakery on China Street. The cafe's skilled baristas are happy to talk guests through the options (these change almost daily) and recommend the best prep methods and flavour pairings.

Established
2019

Key roaster
Atkinsons
Coffee Roasters

Brewing method
Espresso, V60,
batch brew

Machine
Victoria Arduino
Eagle One

Grinder
Mahlkonig E65S

Opening hours
Mon–Sun
10am–4.45pm

REUSABLES ACCEPTED   WIFI   BIKE FRIENDLY   BUY BEANS IN STORE   OUTDOOR SEATING

10 ATKINSONS THE HALL

10 China Street, Lancaster, Lancashire, LA1 1EX

thecoffeehopper.com | 01524 65470

f *thehallcafe* *ⓞ* *atkinsons.coffee*

The flagship venue of Lancashire powerhouse Atkinsons Coffee Roasters, The Hall is where coffee lovers go to sample complex roasts and watch baristas work their magic on the mesmerising syphon brewers.

Atkinsons owners Ian and Sue Steel have transformed the 1930s former parish hall into a cathedral for speciality fans. The dynamic selection of seasonal blends and single-origin beans is roasted next door at the roastery (ask nicely and you might get a peek inside) and prepared in various methods including espresso, batch brew and Chemex.

TIP POP INTO THE SHOP NEXT DOOR TO PICK UP BEANS, CHOCOLATE AND OTHER GOODIES

The Hall is equally popular with locals and those looking for a welcoming spot in which to spend an hour relaxing or catching up on work. Its beautiful design (featuring original Canadian maple-wood floors and vaulted ceilings) and unpretentious baristas (who are as happy to craft a cappuccino as they are a super-clean syphon) make it a perennially popular spot.

The adjoining sister bakery stocks the counter with cakes and pastries, and there's a daily selection of sandwiches and toasties. The flavour combinations are constantly evolving, so expect specials such as chocolate stout loaf and burnt Basque cheesecake.

Established
2012

Key roaster
Atkinsons
Coffee Roasters

Brewing method
Espresso, syphon,
batch brew,
Chemex

Machine
Sanremo Café Racer

Grinder
Mahlkonig E65S,
Mahlkonig EK43

Opening hours
Mon–Sat
9am–5pm
Sun
9am–4.30pm

REUSABLES
ACCEPTED
WIFI
BIKE
FRIENDLY
DOGS
WELCOME
BUY BEANS
IN STORE

II ATKINSONS THE MUSIC ROOM

Sun Square, Sun Street, Lancaster, Lancashire, LA1 1EW

thecoffeehopper.com | 01524 65470

f *themusicroomcafe* **◎** *atkinsons.coffee*

If The Hall is the place to hunker down and shelter from the elements in Lancaster, then The Music Room is your go-to when the city is bathed in sunshine. Overlooking the aptly named Sun Square, the petite cafe space is the little sister site to Atkinsons' flagship cafe, roastery and shop on China Street.

With floor-to-ceiling windows allowing light to flood the sleek Scandi-style fixtures and furnishings, the Grade II-listed Rococo pavilion is a uniquely elegant spot at which to enjoy refined speciality coffee. House blends and limited-edition single origins are prepared by skilled baristas in a variety of brewing methods including espresso, V60 and batch brew.

TIP A MEZZANINE FLOOR OFFERS ADDITIONAL INDOOR SEATING ON COLD OR DRIZZLY DAYS

On dry days, the courtyard fills with locals and visitors who take advantage of the plentiful alfresco seating. Seasonal drinks such as cold brew and tonic offer caffeinated refreshment on warm afternoons, while beautiful cakes and pastries from the Atkinsons bakery will brighten your day whatever the weather.

Established
2010

Key roaster
Atkinsons
Coffee Roasters

Brewing method
Espresso, V60,
batch brew,
cold brew

Machine
La Marzocco FB80

Grinder
Mahlkonig E65S

Opening hours
Mon–Sat
10am–4pm

LANCASTER

REUSABLES ACCEPTED WIFI BIKE FRIENDLY DOGS WELCOME BUY BEANS IN STORE OUTDOOR SEATING

40

12 JOURNEY SOCIAL KITCHEN

28 New Street, Lancaster, Lancashire, LA1 1EG

journeysocial.co.uk | 07561 550255

journeysociallancaster

Don't be surprised if you have to wait for a table at this buzzy brunch spot that's loved for its inventive take on weekend dining. However, queuing is no biggie when you know lip-smacking dishes await such as Calabrian 'nduja mac and cheese on toasted brioche with fried egg and pickled onions.

The cafe's unwavering popularity has recently resulted in a move to bigger premises on New Street, yet despite the increase in covers Journey Social's first-class service remains on point. Whether you visit at peak time (weekend mornings) or a Monday afternoon, quality is assured from the moment you're shown to your table to the clearing of your last empty plate.

TIP CHECK OUT JOURNEY'S NEW FINE-DINING VENTURE, NOW OR NEVER

A high-calibre cafe experience requires an above-par drinks menu and Journey Social doesn't disappoint. The speciality coffee line-up is headlined by London's Allpress Espresso, while guest roasts from Red Bank in Kendal are available as V60.

The elegant minimalist interior (bright white walls, booth seating and sleek marble-style tabletops) creates an irresistibly Instagrammable backdrop for brunch.

Established
2018

Key roaster
Allpress Espresso

Brewing method
Espresso, V60

Machine
La Marzocco
Linea PB

Grinder
Victoria Arduino
Mythos One

Opening hours
Mon–Sat
9am–5pm
Sun
9.30am–4pm

 REUSABLES ACCEPTED   BIKE FRIENDLY   DOGS WELCOME   BUY BEANS IN STORE   COFFEE COURSES   OUTDOOR SEATING

LANCASTER

41

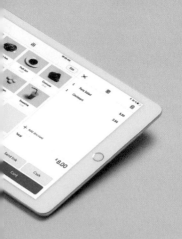

Tools to run your coffee shop

Zettle
by PayPal

zettle.com/gb/contact-us

13 RISE - PRESTON

15 Miller Arcade, Preston, Lancashire, PR1 2QY

risebrunch.co.uk

f risebrunch *⊙ risebrunch*

Brunch is more than just a meal at this buzzy Preston cafe: it's an opportunity to slow down, de-stress and reconnect with your favourite people as you tuck into delicious breakfast-based dishes.

Inspired by the antipodean coffee scene, Rise is light, bright and designed around a mix of intimate tables and larger benches that make it the perfect setting for all manner of social occasions. The menu, which includes Insta-ready delights such as breakfast rolls, turkish eggs and smoothie bowls, also draws influence from Down Under.

TIP A NEW SISTER VENUE, LOCATED 700 YARDS AWAY, OPENS IN SUMMER 2023

The coffee is crafted by Ozone, one of the pioneering New Zealand roasteries that kick-started the speciality movement in the late nineties. Beans destined for Rise's grinder are roasted at Ozone's London HQ and prepared in Preston as espresso and cold brew.

Service is slick yet friendly and guests are encouraged to kick back and enjoy the experience – the baristas are always happy to share good pairings or explain serve styles. There's often a queue for a table (especially on Saturdays and Sundays, when weekend specials make the brunch bill even more enticing), but the wait is always brief and worthwhile.

Established
2019

Key roaster
Ozone Coffee

Brewing method
Espresso, cold brew

Machine
La Marzocco
Linea PB

Grinder
Mazzer Kold S

Opening hours
Mon-Fri
8am–5pm
Sat-Sun
9am–5pm

REUSABLES
ACCEPTED   WIFI   BIKE
FRIENDLY   BUY BEANS
IN STORE   OUTDOOR
SEATING

14 FOUR ONE TWO

412 Blackburn Road, Higher Wheelton, Chorley, Lancashire, PR6 8HX

01254 433500

f *fouronetwocafe* ⊙ *four.1.two*

Sip a silky flat white, munch on a warm-from-the-oven pastry, browse unusual gifts or even pick up flowers at this new hybrid venue in Higher Wheelton.

Four One Two is a collaboration between two families: Sophie manages the florist and gift shop while husband-and-wife team Scott and Bex run the cafe. Before teaming up with Sophie, Scott worked in the speciality coffee industry for over a decade (placing second in the 2018 World Coffee in Good Spirits Championship) and Bex ran a successful bakery. High-calibre caffeine and cake is therefore a given.

TIP LOOK OUT FOR FUTURE POP-UP EVENTS WITH LOCAL BUSINESSES

The house espresso is an exclusive blend crafted by Holmfirth newbie Danelaw Coffee. Sample it straight up or matched with steamed milk in a luxurious latte and pair your pick with one of Bex's freshly made bakes.

Don't leave without checking out the retail shelves of local artisan food and drink products or picking up a bunch of blooms to take the good vibes home with you.

Established
2022

Key roaster
Danelaw Coffee

Brewing method
Espresso, V60,
AeroPress

Machine
Conti CC100

Grinder
Mazzer Kony S

Opening hours
Mon, Wed–Fri
8am–4pm
Sat
9am–4pm
Sun
10am–4pm

CHORLEY

WIFI BIKE FRIENDLY DOGS WELCOME COFFEE COURSES

44

15 BLOOM & BREW

22-24 Church Street, Ormskirk, Lancashire, L39 3AN

bloomandbrew.co.uk | 07341 665482

f bloomandbrewuk *◎ bloomandbrewuk*

Everything you drink, eat or buy at Bloom & Brew has been curated and crafted with sustainability in mind. Charlotte Brennan and Paul Seagraves have blended an indie coffee shop with a sustainable homeware store and refill station to create a unique space to meet and shop.

Visit to enjoy coffee roasted by Liverpool's Neighbourhood Coffee paired with decadent bakes, such as Biscoff cronuts, sourced from a roster of local bakeries. To minimise waste, milk is supplied in a closed-loop system and guest brews from the likes of Girls Who Grind, Dark Arts, 92 Degrees and Bean Coffee are sourced in refillable 12-litre tubs. Those who arrive armed with a reusable cup receive a discount on takeaway drinks.

TIP AN ONLINE SHOP IS IN THE PIPELINE

Those wanting to spoil themselves or a loved one with a stylish-yet-sustainable gift will want to factor in time to peruse the handcrafted items, which range from homewares and jewellery to dried flowers and eco-friendly pet accessories. There are also refill stations for herbs, spices, pasta, nuts, shampoo and cleaning liquids, so don't forget to take containers with you.

Established
2021

Key roaster
Neighbourhood
Coffee

Brewing method
Espresso, filter

Machine
La Marzocco
Linea Classic

Grinder
Anfim Pratica

Opening hours
Tue-Sat
9.30am-4pm

REUSABLES
ACCEPTED

WIFI

DOGS
WELCOME

BUY BEANS
IN STORE

OUTDOOR
SEATING

ORMSKIRK

45

16 CROSBY COFFEE - OXFORD ROAD

2 Oxford Road, Waterloo, Liverpool, Merseyside, L22 8QF

crosbycoffee.co.uk | 01515 385454

f crosbycoffeeltd ⓞ *crosbycoffeeltd*

Crosby Coffee is something of a community hub in Waterloo, hosting friends for catch-ups fuelled by flat whites and croissants, remote workers looking to escape the home office, and new mums craving caffeinated respite.

The newly renovated basement seating area (which previously housed the roastery training space before it moved to new premises) is lined with benches and plugs to keep laptops powered, as well as comfy sofas and seating for laidback loungers.

TIP THE CAFE IS SUPER DOG-FRIENDLY SO DON'T BE AFRAID TO PITCH UP WITH YOUR POOCH

The real selling point, however, is the coffee, which is all roasted in-house using sustainably sourced beans from Africa and South America. In the grinders at this Oxford Road outpost is a choice of three house blends, four single origins and a regularly updated limited-edition roast. Speciality drinks are complemented by pastries and cookies from local artisan bakeries.

All of the beans at the bar are available as retail packs to take home or can be delivered direct via a monthly subscription service.

Established
2017

Key roaster
Crosby Coffee Roasters

Brewing method
Espresso, pourover, AeroPress

Machine
Conti MC Ultima

Grinder
Compak E8 DBW, Compak E8, Compak E6, Mahlkonig EK43

Opening hours
Mon–Fri
8am–5pm
Sat–Sun
9am–4pm

LIVERPOOL

REUSABLES ACCEPTED | WIFI | BIKE FRIENDLY | DOGS WELCOME | BUY BEANS IN STORE | COFFEE COURSES | OUTDOOR SEATING

46

17 BEAN COFFEE ROASTERS - LIVERPOOL ONE

18-20 College Lane, Liverpool, Merseyside, L1 3DS
beancoffee.co.uk | 01513 759721
f beancoffeeuk *beancoffeeuk*

Located in the heart of Liverpool's shopping district, this is one of 16 Bean Coffee Roasters outposts across the North West (the first opened in 2008). What makes this particular venue unique, however, is that the beans pulled through the Faema are roasted just a mile down the road at its roastery on Brunswick Dock.

The house coffee, Bean Blend, is a chocolatey and red-berry-forward combo of Brazilian, Nicaraguan and Indian beans. It's kept company by a steady roster of single origins, which can be ground to order in store.

TIP TAKE A REUSABLE CUP FOR YOUR TAKEAWAY COFFEE AND GET DOUBLE LOYALTY-CARD STAMPS

At the Bean Coffee brew bar, visitors can try out the different roasts before buying them to take home. They can also see how each one fares when served in different styles – ideal for those who want to expand their coffee-making know-how and experiment with new flavours and brewing techniques (lots of coffee gear is also available to buy in store).

Beyond all the coffee geekery, this is also a very handy place in which to rest and refuel after a day of retail therapy – the freshly made sandwiches and cinnamon buns are especially good.

REUSABLES ACCEPTED | WIFI | DOGS WELCOME | BUY BEANS IN STORE | COFFEE COURSES | OUTDOOR SEATING

Established
2021

Key roaster
Bean Coffee Roasters

Brewing method
Espresso, V60, Chemex, cafetiere, AeroPress, syphon, batch brew

Machine
Faema President

Grinder
Mahlkonig EK43, Mahlkonig E65S, Mazzer Robur S, Mahlkonig E80 GbW

Opening hours
Mon-Sat
7.30am-8pm
Sun
10am-6pm

18 CROSBY COFFEE - LARK LANE

62 Lark Lane, Aigburth, Liverpool, Merseyside, L17 8UP

crosbycoffee.co.uk | 01515 385454

f crosbycoffeeltd *⊙ crosbycoffeeltd*

In 2021, Crosby Coffee opened its second bricks-and-mortar coffee shop in the leafy Liverpool suburb of Aigburth. The team have made the most of the narrow venue on Lark Lane, cleverly positioning tables and adding seating to the snug basement area to create a functional yet welcoming cafe space.

As you'd expect from the Crosby crew, the star attraction is the speciality coffee. All of the beans are roasted at Crosby HQ across town, and four grinders give discerning visitors a wide selection of single origins and house blends to choose from. The latest micro-lots are available as pourover or AeroPress.

TIP AN EXCITING NEW FOOD LINE-UP LAUNCHES SOON

Customers looking to brush up their own barista skills can pick up beans, kit and accessories from the well-stocked retail shelves, and perfect their pourover prowess by joining one of the regular manual brewing workshops.

The food offering is simple and designed to complement the coffee: bouncy buttery cruffins from The Butterholic in Kirkby are ever popular, as is the selection of cakes and cookies from Bootle's Dumb Dough.

Established
2021

Key roaster
Crosby Coffee Roasters

Brewing method
Espresso, pourover, AeroPress

Machine
Conti MC Ultima

Grinder
Compak E8 DBW, Compak E8, Compak E6, Mahlkonig EK43

Opening hours
Mon–Fri
8am–5pm
Sat–Sun
9am–4pm

LIVERPOOL

REUSABLES ACCEPTED | WIFI | BIKE FRIENDLY | DOGS WELCOME | BUY BEANS IN STORE | OUTDOOR SEATING

19 PRESS BROS COFFEE

82 Lark Lane, Liverpool, Merseyside, L17 8UU

pressbros.co.uk | 07875 322228

pressbroscoffee

Brothers Oliver and Tito Press began their speciality journey in 2017, serving coffee from a converted Piaggio van at Liverpool's Baltic Market. By 2021 they had outgrown their original set-up and relocated to this roomier bricks-and-mortar site on indie-centric Lark Lane.

Considering the brothers hadn't a clue about crafting coffee before they bought the van, and learnt how to get their 'spros up to snuff on the fly, the quality of coffee at Press Bros is quite astonishing.

Experience the team's espresso excellence when you order the house blend Pour (a bespoke roast from Liverpool's Neighbourhood Coffee) as a flat white, or put their pourover skills through their paces by sampling the current guest coffee as V60 or AeroPress.

TIP CHECK OUT THE REGULAR SUPPER CLUBS, DJ NIGHTS AND WEEKLY CHESS CLUB

Hungry? The Press Bros' scran is as good as its coffee. Bolster your order with one of the breakfast muffins – the sausage-patty melt and bacon, egg and cheese combos are customer faves.

Established
2017

Key roaster
Neighbourhood Coffee

Brewing method
Espresso, V60, AeroPress

Machine
La Marzocco KB90

Grinder
Mahlkonig E80 Extreme, Mahlkonig EK43

Opening hours
Mon–Sun
9am–5pm

WIFI | BIKE FRIENDLY | DOGS WELCOME | BUY BEANS IN STORE

20 BEAN THERE COFFEE SHOP

374-376 Smithdown Road, Wavertree, Liverpool, Merseyside, L15 5AN
beantherecoffeeshop.com | 01513 093046
f beantherecoffeeshop *beantherecoffeeshop*

The Bean There bunch have had a busy year, headlined by the opening of the Bean There Bakery across town on Rose Lane. Those stopping at the flagship venue for a toastie (the ham hock, caramelised onion, spinach and cheddar combo on house sourdough is the bestseller) or a slice of something sweet will enjoy knowing it was freshly baked that morning at the new sister site.

TIP FIRST BREW OF THE DAY? PAIR IT WITH A BUTTERY PRALINE PAIN AU CHOCOLAT

This friendly neighbourhood cafe's bakes are equalled only by its champion coffee offering. Alongside house beans for espresso from roasting heavyweight Atkinsons, single-origin offerings come courtesy of a carousel of UK roasteries and are available to sample as batch, V60 or Chemex. Recent highlights have come from fellow northerners Neighbourhood and Blossom.

The Bean There feast for the senses is heightened by regular art exhibitions, craft workshops and events – keep an eye on social for upcoming dates.

Established
2017

Key roaster
Atkinsons
Coffee Roasters

Brewing method
Espresso, V60,
batch brew,
Chemex

Machine
La Marzocco
Linea PB

Grinder
Victoria Arduino
Mythos One,
Mahlkonig EK43

Opening hours
Mon-Fri
8am-5pm
Sat-Sun
9am-5pm

REUSABLES
ACCEPTED

WIFI

BIKE
FRIENDLY

DOGS
WELCOME

BUY BEANS
IN STORE

OUTDOOR
SEATING

LIVERPOOL

50

21 SUP

6 Atherton Street, New Brighton, Wirral, Merseyside, CH45 2NY
wearesupshop.com | 07545 138081
f wearesup *⊙ wearesupshop*

P air your espresso with a healthy helping of creative inspiration at this unusual (but super friendly) cafe in the seaside town of New Brighton. As well as being a hotspot for fabulous coffee and fodder, SUP is also a bottleshop and retail space with an adjoining print studio where owners Luce and Scott design a range of quirky screen prints which are displayed around the shop.

Browse shelves stacked with cards, craft beers, natural wines, candles and other gifts, then take a seat to enjoy an espresso-based drink crafted from Hundred House beans. There are also guest roast options from the likes of Girls Who Grind.

TIP PICK UP A BAG OF THE GUEST COFFEE IN THE SHOP

Being sociable is positively encouraged at SUP and the venue has an authentic community vibe. The events calendar is packed with everything from workshops and wine tasting evenings to beer running clubs and pizza parties in collaboration with the Dough Bros.

Dogs are very welcome and in with a chance of being crowned as 'SUP dog of the day', which runs on the cafe's Insta feed.

Established
2020

Key roaster
Hundred
House Coffee

Brewing method
Espresso

Machine
La Marzocco
Linea Classic

Grinder
Anfim SCODY

Opening hours
Wed–Sat
10am–9pm
Sun
10am–5pm

WIFI   DOGS WELCOME   BUY BEANS IN STORE   OUTDOOR SEATING

22 LATERAL

83 Banks Road, West Kirby, Wirral, Merseyside, CH48 0RA

wyldecoffee.com

f lateralbywylde *☺ lateralcafe*

When Jamie McIlhatton and Warren Norton opened Wylde in Heswall in 2019, their aim was to create a cafe space where folks who take pleasure in slowing down to enjoy good coffee and conversation could convene.

The pair pulled it off with great success so, two years later, they found themselves launching Lateral in West Kirby. Like its older sibling, the experience at this lifestyle cafe is built around expertly crafted coffee from Liverpool roastery Neighbourhood (plus a roster of guests). Jamie and Warren's chilled-out and friendly vibe also influences how customers interact with each other, as Jamie explains: *'You'll often see complete strangers turning their chairs around to chat to each other.'*

TIP CHECK OUT THE WYLDE BAKERY IN BEBINGTON FOR CRACKING COFFEE AND CAKES

This second site diverges from the original after sundown (Tuesday to Saturday) when mochas are switched for Margaritas as Lateral dons its alter ego as a cocktail bar.

Night or day, it's a great spot for gathering – whether to sample the latest pop-up offering (such as the recent Mexican menu) or to take part in the weekly quiz.

Established
2021

Key roaster
Neighbourhood Coffee

Brewing method
Espresso, batch brew

Machine
La Marzocco Linea PB AV

Grinder
Victoria Arduino Mythos One

Opening hours
Tue–Sat
8.30am–10pm
Sun–Mon
8.30am–5pm

REUSABLES ACCEPTED | WIFI | BIKE FRIENDLY | DOGS WELCOME | BUY BEANS IN STORE | OUTDOOR SEATING

WEST KIRBY

23 WYLDE COFFEE

86 Telegraph Road, Heswall, Wirral, Merseyside, CH60 0AQ

wyldecoffee.com

f wyldecoffee *⊙ wyldecafe*

Oldest siblings are sometimes (unfairly) branded as bossy and outspoken, while simultaneously being vaunted for their determination and sense of responsibility. And Wylde – the big sis of a trio of coffee shops created by Jamie McIlhatton and Warren Norton – certainly fits the latter description.

The crew are big on taking responsibility for their impact on the planet so coffee is supplied in 100 per cent biodegradable bags created from wood pulp, as well as in reusable containers.

An appreciation of nature also comes through in the house beans, roasted by Neighbourhood in Liverpool, which are named after British birds. The espresso blend, Housemartin, is made up of natural Brazilian and washed Colombian beans.

TIP HUNGRY? ORDER A SLAB OF SOURDOUGH PILED WITH TEMPTING TOPPINGS

Visit for a relaxed cafe vibe and an unpretentious attitude to speciality coffee and, if you like the Wylde approach, get a further hit at sister coffee shop Lateral in West Kirby and the Wylde Bakery in Bebington where most of the cakes are crafted.

Established
2019

Key roaster
Neighbourhood Coffee

Brewing method
Espresso, batch brew

Machine
La Marzocco Linea PB AV

Grinder
Victoria Arduino Mythos One

Opening hours
Mon-Fri
8am-4pm
Sat-Sun
9am-4pm

REUSABLES ACCEPTED

WIFI

BIKE FRIENDLY

DOGS WELCOME

BUY BEANS IN STORE

OUTDOOR SEATING

HESWALL

53

CUMBRIA,
LANCASHIRE
& MERSEYSIDE

ROASTERIES

24 RINALDO'S SPECIALITY COFFEE & FINE TEA

Unit 12 Lakeland Food Park, Crook Road, Kendal, Cumbria, LA8 8QJ

rinscoffee.com | 07799 115775

f *rinscoffee* ⓘ *rinscoffee*

Dedicated to roasting small-batch beans, this Kendal roastery and espresso bar sources sustainably farmed coffees from across the growing belt.

The locals' favourite is its Great Taste award-winning house house blend, Casa – a mix of Brazilian and El Salvadoran beans, which the judging panel described as having *'wonderfully pronounced toasted peanut flavours ... evocative of pad thai'*.

As well as crafting a wide spectrum of coffees on their Giesen W15A, the team source and sell an assortment of loose-leaf teas. Own-roasted beans and blended teas can be sampled at the roastery's espresso bar and shop, where a lust-worthy selection of ECM, Ascaso and Gaggia machines are also displayed.

'WONDERFULLY PRONOUNCED PEANUT FLAVOURS ... EVOCATIVE OF PAD THAI'

Visitors will also get to meet the business' new owner, entrepreneur Jayne Hynes, who bought the roastery in October 2022 from retiring founder Rinaldo Columbi. Alongside espousing the joys of speciality coffee to all who pass through this gateway to the Lake District, Jayne plans to grow the wholesale and online arms of the enterprise.

Established
2015

Roaster make and size
Giesen W15A 15kg

KENDAL

CAFE
ON SITE

OPEN BY
INVITE

COFFEE
COURSES

BUY BEANS
ONLINE

BUY BEANS
IN STORE

56

25 CARRINGTONS COFFEE CO.

Unit 14c Keer Park, Warton Road, Carnforth, Lancashire, LA5 9FG

carringtonscoffee.co | 07880 611027

f *carringtonscoffee* ⊙ *carringtonscoffeeco*

Founded in 2019 by Suzy and Alex Carrington, Carringtons Coffee Co. is the result of a transformative trip to a friend's coffee farm in Colombia. Returning to the UK with a new passion for quality coffee and a commitment to building community, the duo established a roastery in Carnforth and began importing beans.

After four years in business, Carringtons has become an integral part of the Morecambe Bay coffee scene and not only offers a catalogue of seven distinct coffees but also serves as a unique event space for the local community. Highlights in the coffee collection include Doghouse (its bestselling and totally dependable single-estate Brazilian espresso) and PB&J (a comforting nutty blend with a touch of jammy sweetness).

Established
2019

Roaster make and size
Giesen W15A 15kg

'A BOLD NEW BLEND FEATURING SPECIALITY-GRADE ROBUSTA BEANS'

Suzy and Alex recently introduced Fuelling the Bold, which is a new vision for Carringtons' future in the coffee industry. Inspired by their belief in the power of courageous living, they've launched a bold new blend featuring speciality-grade robusta beans and are hosting events that foster community building.

'At Carringtons, coffee is more than just a speciality experience. It's an opportunity to connect with others and celebrate the boldness that fuels us all,' says Suzy.

OPEN TO THE PUBLIC

BUY BEANS ONLINE

BUY BEANS IN STORE

26 ATKINSONS COFFEE ROASTERS

12 China Street, Lancaster, Lancashire, LA1 1EX

thecoffeehopper.com | 01524 65470

f atkinsonscoffee ⓘ *atkinsons.coffee*

Tradition meets innovation at this historic coffee roastery in the heart of Lancaster. Originally established in 1837 as The Grasshopper Tea House, Atkinsons is one of the oldest roasteries in the UK.

Since taking over in 2005, Ian and Sue Steel have reinvigorated the brand and pulled it into the 21st century. Today it's one of the most respected speciality roasters in the country, renowned for its reliably delicious blends and revolving seasonal single-origins which are roasted on a super-low-emission Loring Kestrel.

'ONE OF THE MOST RESPECTED SPECIALITY ROASTERS IN THE COUNTRY'

For almost two decades, the Atkinsons team have been dedicated to building long-lasting relationships with producers around the world, including in Guatemala, Brazil, Ethiopia, Costa Rica, Sumatra, Rwanda and Colombia. A particularly close partnership with Café Granja La Esperanza in Colombia results in a regular delivery of rare and interesting varietals which have been processed using different fermentation methods.

The best place to sample Atkinsons' beans is at one of its three excellent cafes in Lancaster. Pay a visit to The Hall on China Street to taste the brews and then browse coffees and artisan goods in the original shop next door. Coffee-curious folk and wholesale customers will soon be able to go behind the scenes of the on-site roastery when the new training room is complete.

Established
1837

Roaster make and size
Loring Kestrel 35kg

LANCASTER

CAFE ON SITE

BUY BEANS ONLINE

BUY BEANS IN STORE

27 CROSBY COFFEE ROASTERS

Units 2-3 Lockwoods Trading Estate, Bridle Way, Liverpool, Merseyside, L30 4UA

crosbycoffee.co.uk | 01515 385454

f crosbycoffee ⊙ *crosbycoffeeltd*

Manual brewing, latte art, sensory cupping and milk texturing are just a few of the skills aspiring baristas and caffeine enthusiasts can learn to perfect at Crosby Coffee's ever-expanding roastery. Such is the demand for its coffee that the whole roastery set-up recently relocated from its original HQ on Oxford Road to an industrial estate in Aintree.

The new and roomier premises enabled the team to buy a hulking 30kg Toper roaster to bronze their growing range of blends and single origins. There's also more space for a new training area for wholesale customers and members of the public.

Beans are sustainably sourced direct from farmers across South America and Africa. The signature Iron Man blend fuses beans from Guatemala, Honduras and Brazil into a rich and smooth concoction with notes of hazelnut and dark chocolate.

'A NEW TRAINING AREA FOR WHOLESALE CUSTOMERS AND MEMBERS OF THE PUBLIC'

The Crosby crew are known for never resting on their laurels and continue to invest in experimental coffee processes to bring ever-more interesting roasts to Liverpool's speciality scene. Exciting batches include the Colombian Santa Monica (where beans are rested in aged rum barrels) and Finca Villarazo (where wine yeast and fresh strawberries are added to the fermentation process).

Established
2014

Roaster make and size
Toper 30kg,
Toper 10kg

COFFEE COURSES

BUY BEANS ONLINE

BUY BEANS IN STORE

LIVERPOOL

59

28 NEIGHBOURHOOD COFFEE

Unit 22 Sandon Estate, Sandon Way, Liverpool, Merseyside, L5 9YN
neighbourhoodcoffee.co.uk | 01512 366741

f *neighbourhoodcoffee* ◎ *neighbourhoodcoffee*

Nothing raises the spirits quite like belting out an 80s classic, and this Liverpool roastery's beans – which take their names from seminal smash hits – provide the perfect prompt for those who need a perk-me-up while preparing their morning coffee.

Headlining the collection is Espresso Yourself (the popular house blend also available in Nespresso-compatible pods), with support from the likes of Born Sippin' (a light natural Ethiopian) and Kiss From A Roast (a rich washed Indian). Even the decaf, (I Can't Get No) Caffeination, delivers a dose of musical nostalgia.

Established
2014

Roaster make and size
Giesen W60A 60kg,
Giesen W15A 15kg

'13 GREAT TASTE AWARDS IN THE PAST THREE YEARS'

While founders and former green-bean buyers Edward and Chris like to keep things fun, their core focus is on crafting high-quality, accessible coffee. Having collected 13 Great Taste awards in the past three years, their hard work has clearly paid off.

Six different subscriptions cater for those keen on convenience, and includes a Roasters Choice option, which showcases exclusive one-off coffees. Want to get lost down the coffee rabbit hole? Book onto a barista training course or an in-depth brewing class.

LIVERPOOL

OPEN BY INVITE   **BUY BEANS ONLINE**   **BUY BEANS IN STORE**

29 BEAN COFFEE ROASTERS

Summers Road, Brunswick Business Park, Liverpool, Merseyside, L3 4BL

beancoffee.co.uk | 01519 095782

f beancoffeeuk *⊙ beancoffeeuk*

Located on Liverpool's historic Brunswick Dock, the roastery arm of North West coffee-shop enterprise Bean Coffee Roasters is going from strength to strength. First opened in 2015, the roastery not only supplies fresh coffee to its 16 cafes but is also enjoying a growing wholesale business and online subscription offering.

Established
2015

Roaster make and size
Loring 35kg, Petroncini 15kg

'THE TEAM ARE COMMITTED TO GIVING BACK TO THEIR COMMUNITY'

The team meticulously select speciality beans from across the coffee-growing belt, sourcing both direct from farmers and through trusted importers. The breadth of these partnerships means there's a constantly evolving range of single origins on offer at any time. The house Bean Blend is a double Great Taste award winner and can be supplied in customers' preferred grind size or in Nespresso-compatible pods.

As well as knocking out consistently good coffee, the team are committed to giving back to their community. The crew are longtime supporters of Liverpool's Alder Hey Children's Charity and recently donated £5 from the sale of every bag of Oli's Blend, a limited-edition coffee named after the charity's mascot.

OPEN BY INVITE

BUY BEANS ONLINE

BUY BEANS IN STORE

LIVERPOOL

GREATER MANCHESTER & CHESHIRE

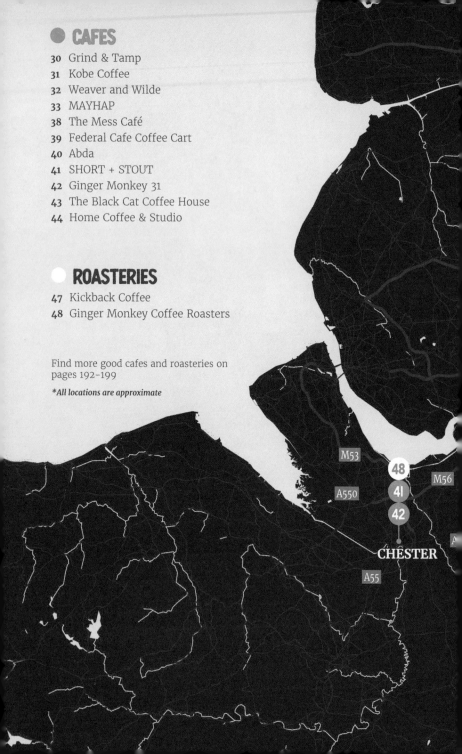

● CAFES

● ROASTERIES

Find more good cafes and roasteries on pages 192–199

All locations are approximate

M53

A550

M56

48

4I

42

CHESTER

A55

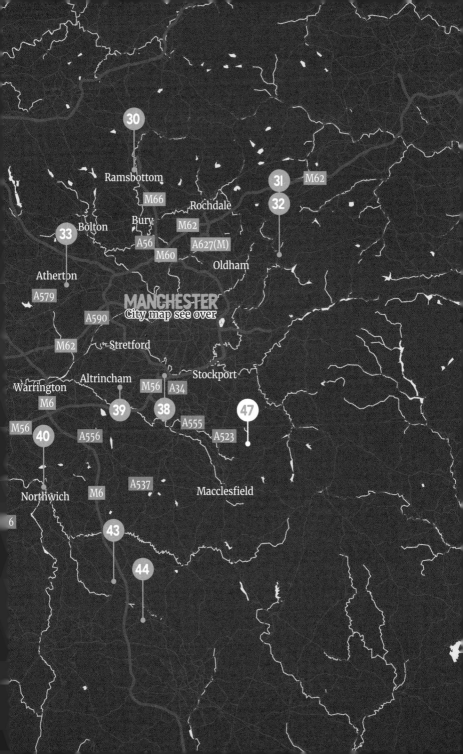

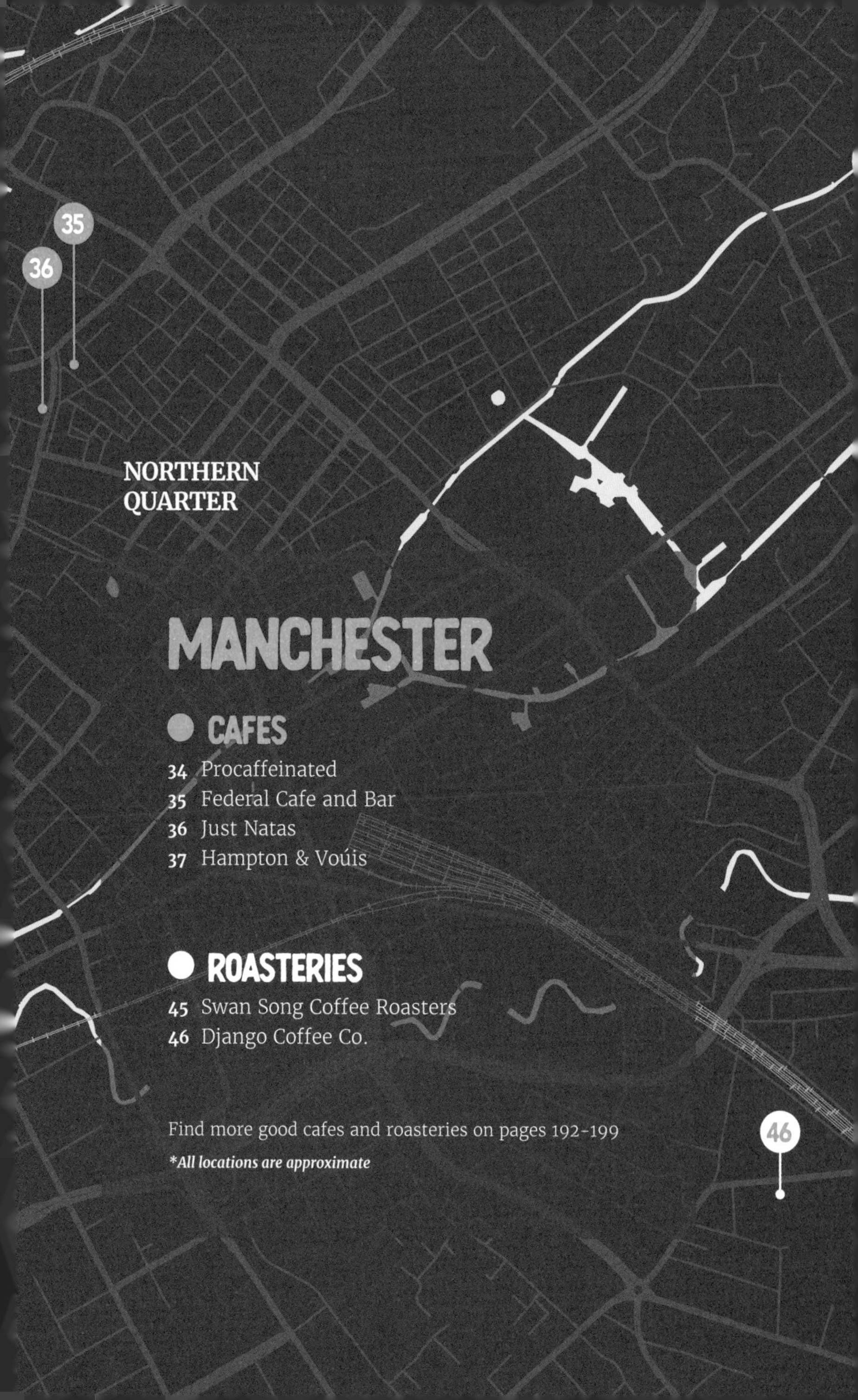
35
36
NORTHERN QUARTER
MANCHESTER
CAFES
34 Procaffeinated
35 Federal Cafe and Bar
36 Just Natas
37 Hampton & Voúis
ROASTERIES
45 Swan Song Coffee Roasters
46 Django Coffee Co.
Find more good cafes and roasteries on pages 192-199
*All locations are approximate
46

30 GRIND & TAMP

45 Bridge Street, Ramsbottom, Bury, Greater Manchester, BL0 9AD
grindandtamp.co.uk | 07359 396446
f grindandtampcoffee Ⓞ *grind_tamp*

If you're anywhere near the market town of Ramsbottom, it's definitely worth making a detour to sample the top-drawer coffee at this popular coffee shop.

The Grind & Tamp team are on point with their bean selection and brewing methods, and every visit will unveil new flavours to try from roasteries such as Hard Lines, Red Bank, ALLCAPS and Obadiah. The gang recently collaborated with long-standing Lancashire stalwart Atkinsons to create their house coffee, which is available in espresso-based drinks and for customers to take home in refillable canisters. With every refill sold the cafe donates ten per cent of profits to Project Waterfall, a charity that helps provide clean water to coffee-growing communities.

TIP EXPERIENCE THE CLASSY COFFEE IN A HOUSE ESPRESSO MARTINI

While speciality coffee takes centre stage at Grind & Tamp, it's shored up by an informal menu of delicious brunch dishes, light bites and home bakes. Swing by in the morning and mop up turkish eggs and lamb sausages with slices of sourdough. In the afternoon, nibble on pastel de nata as you catch up with friends over a brew.

Established
2016

Key roaster
Atkinsons
Coffee Roasters

Brewing method
Espresso, V60,
Chemex, AeroPress,
batch brew

Machine
Sanremo Café Racer

Grinder
Mythos One,
Mahlkonig E65S
GbW,
DIP DK-30

Opening hours
Mon-Fri
8am-4pm
Sat
8.30am-4pm
Sun
10am-3pm

WIFI   DOGS WELCOME   BUY BEANS IN STORE   COFFEE COURSES

RAMSBOTTOM

3| KOBE COFFEE

36 High Street, Uppermill, Oldham, Greater Manchester, OL3 6HR

kobecoffee.co.uk | 01457 761861

f kobecoffeeuppermill *◎ kobecoffeeuk*

Every village needs a cafe like Kobe Coffee, with a wooden counter stacked with freshly baked cookies and cakes, a food menu crammed with brunch and lunch favourites, and a reliably delicious house espresso in the grinder.

Nestled in the centre of the picturesque village of Uppermill on the edge of Saddleworth Moor, Kobe has a warm and welcoming atmosphere and teems with life thanks to its never-ending stream of customers and abundance of luscious plants.

TIP CHECK OUT SISTER RESTAURANT KOBE ASIA, WHICH SERVES JAPANESE-INSPIRED SMALL PLATES

Perk up weekend mornings by sitting on the sun-dappled terrace with a plate of eggs benedict or a John Street Bakery oven-bottom muffin piled with pork and apple sausages and back bacon. Pair it with a Timber Town seasonal espresso with notes of sweet toffee, chocolate, cashew and zingy citrus (roasted in Nottingham by the team at Outpost), perfectly prepared by the Kobe baristas.

Guest roasts from the likes of North Star, Heart & Graft and Kiss the Hippo ensure there's always something new to try each time you visit.

Established
2019

Key roaster
Outpost Coffee

Brewing method
Espresso, filter

Machine
La Marzocco
Linea Classic

Grinder
Mazzer Robur S,
Mazzer Kony

Opening hours
Mon–Sun
9am–4.30pm

REUSABLES
ACCEPTED

WIFI

DOGS
WELCOME

BUY BEANS
IN STORE

OUTDOOR
SEATING

32 WEAVER AND WILDE

30 High Street, Uppermill, Saddleworth, Greater Manchester, OL3 6HR
weaverandwilde.co.uk | 01457 878222
f weaverandwilde © *weaver_and_wilde*

With its exposed-brick fireplaces, hardwood floors, roaring fire and bustling atmosphere, Weaver and Wilde has the homely feel of a cosy village pub but with a focus on speciality coffee rather than regional ales.

Beans are sourced from Dark Woods Coffee in Huddersfield and paired with milk from Denshaw's McLintock's Dairy in a full spectrum of espresso drinks. There are oat, soy and pea-milk alternatives for those who don't do dairy, plus pourover options for filter fans.

Brunch is a perennial hit with the locals and they can't get enough of signature dishes like tarragon mushrooms on toast and Yorkshire rarebit topped with bubbling Lancashire and manchego cheeses. If you're in the mood for sharing, a selection of small plates delivers the goods.

TIP TREAT YOUR DOG TO THEIR VERY OWN DOGGICCINO

Using a plethora of locally made foodstuffs has long been part of Weaver and Wilde's USP, so it was a no-brainer for owners Thomas and Cal Rowson-Codd to expand their offering to include a new shop in Greenfield which stocks fresh fruit, veg, fish and other provisions.

Established
2019

Key roaster
Dark Woods Coffee

Brewing method
Espresso,
filter, V60,
cafetiere

Machine
La Marzocco
Linea PB

Grinder
Anfim Pratica

Opening hours
Mon–Sun
8am–5pm

REUSABLES ACCEPTED   WIFI   BIKE FRIENDLY   DOGS WELCOME   BUY BEANS IN STORE   COFFEE COURSES

SADDLEWORTH

33 MAYHAP

1 Chapel Street, Tyldesley, Greater Manchester, M29 8FZ

mayhapcoffee.co.uk

f mayhapcoffee *◎ mayhapcoffee*

Stacks of fluffy pancakes drizzled in maple syrup; banoffee and fudge french toast slathered in vanilla mascarpone; 16-hour barbecue beef brisket benedict: this Tyldesley coffee house and kitchen is a haven for those who worship at the altar of brunch.

While the all-day menu offers some of the most indulgent dishes you'll find in the country, owner Matt Whitehead's main focus has always been on serving an excellent cup of coffee.

TIP GET DOWN EARLY TO SNAP UP A PISTACHIO-CREAM-FILLED CROISSANT

Legendary Lancaster roastery Atkinsons rules the house hopper alongside a rotating roster of guest coffees from Round Hill, Hard Lines and Cairngorm, among others. General manager Reece Smith (formerly of Federal Cafe and Bar in Manchester) pours some of the best latte art in the region.

Reece and team relish their part in turning the previously "sleepy" town of Tyldesley into a destination for caffeine tourists. Judging by the ever-increasing number of regulars visiting MAYHAP, it's a feeling shared on both sides of the counter.

Established
2022

Key roaster
Atkinsons Coffee
Roasters

Brewing method
Espresso,
AeroPress, V60,
cafetiere, pourover

Machine
Victoria Arduino
White Eagle

Grinder
Mythos One,
Mahlkonig EK43 S

Opening hours
Mon–Sun
8am–3pm

WIFI   DOGS   BUY BEANS
        WELCOME   IN STORE

TYLDESLEY

71

34 PROCAFFEINATED

263 Chapel Street, Salford, Greater Manchester, M3 5JY

f procaffeinatedmcr *⊙ procaffeinatedmcr*

Procaffeinated owners Daniel Haralambous and Ilaria Criscuolo fell for each other – and speciality coffee – when working together in Amsterdam's coffee scene. The couple returned to the UK and embedded themselves in Manchester's thriving speciality sector before launching their own venture in Salford.

The cafe brings earthy vibes to Chapel Street, thanks to its vaulted ceiling trailing with greenery, huge windows that flood the building with light, and custom-made steel and reclaimed-wood furniture which injects warmth into the industrial styling.

TIP DON'T LEAVE WITHOUT PICKING UP A LOAF OF HOUSE SOURDOUGH FOR LATER

Rather than serving just one house coffee, the team provide two main options: a choc-and-nut bespoke blend from Manchester's Heart & Graft and a fruitier number from Square Mile in London. Adventurous sippers can expand their horizons further via European guest roasts from the likes of Coffee Collective, April, and Andersen & Maillard.

The international theme continues in a Mediterranean-inspired menu where everything – from pesto, sauces and tapenade to sourdough, cakes and pastries – is made in-house.

Established
2022

Key roaster
Multiple roasteries

Brewing method
Espresso,
batch brew,
Clever Dripper

Machine
La Marzocco
Linea PB

Grinder
Mythos One,
Mythos 2

Opening hours
Mon–Fri
8am–4pm
Sat
9am–4pm
Sun
10am–4pm

WIFI | BIKE FRIENDLY | DOGS WELCOME | BUY BEANS IN STORE | OUTDOOR SEATING

35 FEDERAL CAFE AND BAR

9 Nicholas Croft, Northern Quarter, Manchester, M4 1EY

federalcafe.co.uk | 01614 250974

f federalcafebar *⊙ federalcafebar*

An OG of the Manchester speciality scene, Federal Cafe and Bar has been *the* place for on-point espresso and sweet-as french toast for almost a decade.

The popularity of its antipodean-inspired coffee offering and all-day brunch menus has resulted in three Federal outposts in Manchester, as well as sister brands Just Natas (the go-to for silky espresso and golden-topped pastel de nata in Arndale Market) and Federal Coffee Carts in Altrincham and Media City.

TIP NICHOLAS CROFT CAFE FULL? HEAD TO THE SISTER SITE ON DEANSGATE

This Northern Quarter gem is perma-busy, so arrive early to secure a table. Order a flattie made with beans from London's Ozone to sip while you peruse the bill of foodie thrills. The flagship dish is french toast piled with the likes of whipped mascarpone, berries, white chocolate and almonds, but you won't be disappointed if you buck the trend and order steak and eggs with Fed sauce and salsa verde or the cheddar corn fritters with avocado, poached eggs, sweet chilli sauce and sour cream.

Marry your menu selection with a fruity batch brew (also from Ozone) or take a detour via the cocktail list and toast brunch with a Bloody Mary or Espresso Martini.

Established
2014

Key roaster
Ozone Coffee

Brewing method
Espresso, filter

Machine
La Marzocco
Linea PB

Grinder
Mahlkonig E80

Opening hours
Mon-Fri
7.30am-4pm
Sat
8am-5pm
Sun
8am-4pm

REUSABLES ACCEPTED

WIFI

BIKE FRIENDLY

DOGS WELCOME

BUY BEANS IN STORE

COFFEE COURSES

OUTDOOR SEATING

MANCHESTER

36 JUST NATAS

Unit FC2 Arndale Market, 49 High Street, Manchester, M4 3AH

justnatas.com | 07539 581801

f *justnatas* ☉ *just_natas*

It's a bold move to focus on just two items – there's nowhere to hide if they're anything less than exceptional – but the team at Just Natas pull it off with aplomb.

Hidden between the street-food stalls at Arndale Market in the heart of the city, this tiny venue serves one of Europe's most iconic food and drink pairings: pastel de nata and syrupy espresso. The traditional Portuguese custard tarts are baked fresh each morning, giving early birds the opportunity to snaffle them still warm from the oven and crunch through the flaky pastry to the oozing molten centre.

TIP VEGANS REJOICE! THIS IS THE PLACE TO GET YOUR HANDS ON PLANT-BASED PASTEL DE NATA

A crema-rich espresso is the pastry's traditional accompaniment and the Just Natas baristas deliver perfect shots using beans from London roastery Ozone. There's an option to add steamed milk or even a dose of chocolate for a moreish mocha, but we think the contrast of the sweet custard filling with the creamy chocolatey notes of the Hudson espresso blend is too good a pairing to play with.

Established
2020

Key roaster
Ozone Coffee

Brewing method
Espresso

Machine
La Marzocco GS3

Grinder
Mythos One

Opening hours
Mon–Sat
10am–5pm
Sun
11.30am–4pm

REUSABLES
ACCEPTED

BIKE
FRIENDLY

37 HAMPTON & VOÚIS

31 Princess Street, Manchester, M2 4EW

hamptonandvouis.co.uk

☺ *hamptonandvouis*

Escape the bustle of central Manchester and revive your spirits with good coffee and excellent food at this chic cafe that specialises in flexitarian eating.

Regulars praise the squishy vegan pancakes, which come piled with toppings like Biscoff and Bueno or Nutella and bourbon biscuit. The french toast line-up is equally indulgent, with accompaniments including salted caramel, toffee apple and ice cream.

TIP ARRIVE EARLY ON THE WEEKEND TO BEAT THE QUEUE

If savoury is more your scene, there's a broad range of brunch items to pique your appetite. The homemade spicy tomato and garlic beans on toast never disappoints, while carnivores will love the Voúis Madame – toasted sourdough filled with ham and emmental cheese and topped with a poached egg and french-mustard dressing.

Accompanying the all-day brunch plates is a bespoke house coffee from Buxton Coffee Roasters, which reveals notes of hazelnut, chocolate and a hint of citrus. A regular rotation of single origins from guest roasteries is also on hand for those who like to mix things up. Don't forget to pick up a loyalty card and tot up your stamps to claim a free coffee.

Established
2018

Key roaster
Buxton Coffee Roasters

Brewing method
Espresso,
Clever Dripper,
batch brew

Machine
Sanremo Café Racer

Grinder
Mahlkonig E65S
GbW

Opening hours
Mon–Fri
8am–5pm
Sat–Sun
9am–5pm

REUSABLES WIFI DOGS BUY BEANS
ACCEPTED   WELCOME IN STORE

38 THE MESS CAFÉ

Harper Road, Sharston, Manchester, M22 4RG

themessmanchester.co.uk | 01619 469496

f themesscafe *© themesscafe*

People from all walks of life gather at this bright and spacious community hub in Sharston. The not-for-profit cafe offers jobs, training opportunities and a fresh start for ex-offenders and those who've experienced barriers to employment such as refugees, those with additional needs and people who have struggled with addiction or experienced homelessness.

The Mess partners with other indies wherever possible, so its coffee is sourced from Manchester's Heart & Graft roastery, cakes and bakes are crafted at Silver Apples Bakery in Stockport and bread is baked at The Bread Factory in Openshaw. Local produce is put to good use in a line-up of perennial favourites such as turkish eggs, smashed avo and chicken gyros, and a raft of meaty and plant-based burgers (all served until 3pm).

TIP REMOTE WORKERS FLOCK TO THE MESS FOR ITS MANY PLUG SOCKETS, STABLE WIFI AND TOP-NOTCH COFFEE

Surplus food left over at the end of each day is donated to the Community Grocery next door, a church-run organisation that offers food and household items to local families at affordable prices. In the spirit of providing coffee with a purpose, customers can pay it forward by buying a cup for a Community Grocery member which entitles them to a free hot drink.

Established
2013

Key roaster
Heart & Graft

Brewing method
Espresso

Machine
La Marzocco
Linea PB

Grinder
Compak E8 OD

Opening hours
Mon-Fri
8am-4pm
Sat
9am-3pm

REUSABLES ACCEPTED | WIFI | BIKE FRIENDLY | DOGS WELCOME | BUY BEANS IN STORE | OUTDOOR SEATING

SHARSTON

39 FEDERAL CAFE COFFEE CART

Greenwood Street, Altrincham, Cheshire, WA14 1SA

federalcafe.co.uk

f *federalcafebar* ⊙ *federalcafebar*

F ederal Cafe and Bar has been a key player in the Manchester coffee scene for over nine years but has more recently expanded beyond its city-centre locations thanks to two new horseboxes-turned-coffee-carts.

This mobile espresso bar outside Altrincham Market is the original (it hit the streets in 2020), with another recently popping up in Media City. Both are a reliable find for delish espresso-based coffee, seasonal drinks and antipodean treats such as anzac biscuits and Tim Tams.

TIP MISSING OZ? ORDER A CUP OF MILO FOR A DOSE OF AUSTRALASIAN NOSTALGIA

The carts have quickly become indispensable to their local communities due to the quality of the coffee and the friendly baristas, who make an effort to learn regulars' names and orders and engage in friendly chat while preparing the drinks.

Federal's bright yellow branding and kiwi bird logo make the horseboxes easy to spot amid the crowds that often throng outside the market and around the docks.

Established
2020

Key roaster
Ozone Coffee

Brewing method
Espresso

Machine
La Marzocco
Linea PB

Grinder
Mythos One

Opening hours
Mon–Sun
8am–4pm

ALTRINCHAM

WIFI   DOGS   BUY BEANS
        WELCOME IN STORE

40 ABDA

6 Crown Street, Northwich, Cheshire, CW9 5AX

abdas.co.uk | 01606 333813

f abdaalchemists *⊙ abda_alchemists*

Speciality fans searching for a truly unique coffee encounter will find it at this Northwich cafe. From its travel-inspired decor to the lengthy line-up of international coffees and multicultural food menu, Abda celebrates new experiences and inclusivity.

Drawing on her Sudanese/Egyptian and Afro-Arab roots, founder Abda Obeid-Findley wanted to create a *'unique slice of culture and a space for the community where everyone is welcome.'* Since opening in 2018, it's been a roaring success and grown to include a subscription coffee club and sister catering business, Hala.

TIP ARRIVE HUNGRY – THE HUGE MENU OF AFRO-ARAB OCCIDENTAL FUSION DISHES IS NOT TO BE MISSED

Keen to spread the word about speciality coffees that are outside the Western norm, Abda and her team of alchemists (her name for the baristas as *'they do so much more than make coffee'*) showcase a huge range of origins and prepare them in a variety of international serve styles. Alongside the house blend and a decaf, there are usually eight single-origin options which range from darkly roasted Indonesian beans to light, floral Ethiopian coffees.

Education is a key part of the Abda set-up so the cafe hosts regular coffee experiences and courses for everyone to enjoy.

Established
2018

Key roaster
Multiple roasteries

Brewing method
Espresso, V60,
AeroPress, cafetiere

Machine
La Spaziale S40
Suprema

Grinder
Mahlkonig E80,
Mahlkonig EK43,
Anfim SP II

Opening hours
Tue–Sat
9am–4pm

REUSABLES ACCEPTED | WIFI | BIKE FRIENDLY | DOGS WELCOME | BUY BEANS IN STORE | COFFEE COURSES | OUTDOOR SEATING

41 SHORT + STOUT

3a Ermine Road, Hoole, Chester, Cheshire, CH2 3PN

01244 343378

☺ *shortandstoutltd*

With its distinctive red-brick facade and street corner entrance, this neighbourhood coffee shop makes an intriguing first impression before you've even set foot inside. Thankfully the food line-up is equally enticing, luring in customers with its Melbourne-coffee-scene-inspired dishes.

Feast on the likes of a wholesome brunch bowl brimming with veggie haggis, spiced chickpeas, avocado, halloumi, fried eggs and chilli tomato chutney, or chow down on a bagel stuffed with roasted squash, caramelised and crispy onions and sriracha mayo. The anticipation of new antipodean concoctions appearing on the specials board keeps locals coming back week after week.

TIP GOT A FRIEND WHO LOVES COFFEE? BUY THEM A SHORT + STOUT GIFT COIN

While brunch may be the star attraction for many, it would be remiss not to peruse the list of creative bakes on offer. Pull up a pew at one of the bleached-wood tables and enjoy an Ancoats espresso with a slice of deliciously bouncy bundt cake, a decadent white chocolate and raspberry brownie or a slice of freshly baked chai carrot cake. Got a special occasion or an office meeting? Your favourite bakes can also be ordered to take away.

Established
2018

Key roaster
Ancoats Coffee Co.

Brewing method
Espresso,
cold brew

Machine
La Marzocco
Linea PB

Grinder
Mythos One

Opening hours
Mon-Fri
8am-4pm
Sat
9am-4pm
Sun
10am-2pm

REUSABLES ACCEPTED — WIFI — DOGS WELCOME — BUY BEANS IN STORE — OUTDOOR SEATING

42 GINGER MONKEY 31

31 Christleton Road, Boughton, Chester, Cheshire, CH3 5UF

gingermonkeyroasters.com | 01244 350894

f gingermonkeyno31 ◎ gingermonkey_no31

This neighbourhood hangout is the brainchild of coffee connoisseurs Hayley and Cal Hawthorne, who opened their colourful Boughton cafe in 2020.

A major part of Ginger Monkey's appeal is the calibre of its coffee. It's roasted in-house by Cal who sources high-quality beans from across the globe, lightly roasts them until they sing with flavour and then hands them over to talented baristas who brew them as espresso and batch.

TIP SUN SHINING? DINE ALFRESCO ON PASTEL PICNIC BENCHES IN THE COURTYARD

Visitors packing an appetite should pair their coffee with the signature brioche brunch bun: a generous stack of bacon, hash browns and jammy eggs stuffed into a homemade roll. Brioche not your bag? The stuffed bagels make a delicious plan B.

It's also a great place to take little ones, and features a children's menu (including a weaning platter for tinies) and a kids' corner where they can burn off excess energy.

From Friday to Sunday evenings, Ginger Monkey morphs into its bar alter-ego where cocktails, craft beers and wines are served until late.

Established
2020

Key roaster
Ginger Monkey
Coffee Roasters

Brewing method
Espresso,
batch brew

Machine
Biepi MC-E Pro

Grinder
Remidag OD83,
Remidag OD53

Opening hours
Mon–Thu
9am–4pm
Fri–Sun
9am–10pm

REUSABLES ACCEPTED   WIFI   BIKE FRIENDLY   DOGS WELCOME   BUY BEANS IN STORE   OUTDOOR SEATING

43 THE BLACK CAT COFFEE HOUSE

11 Welles Street, Sandbach, Cheshire, CW11 1GT

blackcatcoffeehouse.co.uk | 01270 747737

f *theblackcatcoffeehouse* ◎ *blackcatcoffees*

After a two-decade career in education, headteacher Helen Sweeney pressed the button on a long-held aspiration to run her own coffee shop. Originally pencilled in as a retirement plan, she bit the bullet early and opened the doors to The Black Cat Coffee House in August 2021.

It's a family affair: husband Damien pulls weekend barista shifts and the couple's children help out in their spare time. Helen spends most evenings baking cakes, brownies, muffins and more to ensure the sweet-toothed of Sandbach always have something to get their jaws around.

TIP FOR A SUNDAY TREAT, BOOK THE BLACK CAT'S PROSECCO AFTERNOON TEA

Hasbean's espresso blend Jabberwocky is the house coffee, but a rotating selection of the Stafford roastery's single-origin filters can be ordered via cafetiere – perfect for a lazy morning visit with the papers. Stick around for lunch to sample The Black Cat's homemade focaccia, which comes topped with a medley of fresh ingredients, or try one of the panini, filled baguettes or soups.

Every six weeks or so, the tables are cleared for a live music night featuring wine and nibbles.

Established
2021

Key roaster
Hasbean

Brewing method
Espresso, cafetiere

Machine
Nuova Simonelli Appia Life Compact

Grinder
Mythos One

Opening hours
Mon, Wed–Fri
9am–4pm
Sat
10am–4pm
Sun
10am–3pm

⚡ ⦂Ọ

WIFI BUY BEANS
IN STORE

SANDBACH

83

Organic ACORN DAIRY

DELICIOUSLY YORKSHIRE - BEST
WHOLESALER 2022

QUEEN'S AWARD FOR ENTERPRISE IN
SUSTAINABLE DEVELOPMENT 2021

COMPASSION IN WORLD FARMING AWARD
- GOOD DAIRY AWARD

ETHICAL CONSUMER MAGAZINE - BEST
DAIRY MILK BRAND 2020

FOR BARISTAS
BY ORGANIC COWS

- PERFECT FOR LATTE ART
- COMPLEMENTS COFFEE FLAVOURS
- OPTIMISED FAT AND PROTEIN RATIO
- SMOOTH, LONG-LASTING MICRO FOAM
- AWARD-WINNING SUSTAINABLE METH

acorndairy.c
01325 466

44 HOME COFFEE & STUDIO

16 Lawton Road, Alsager, Cheshire, ST7 2AF

07547 224682

f homecoffeealsager *⊙ homecoffeealsager*

Since opening in August 2022, Home has quickly gained a reputation for bringing some of the UK's best coffee to this sleepy corner of south Cheshire.

With an interior crafted from the imaginings of founder (and architect) Alex Melhuish and wife Nikki, the coffee shop's Scandi decor and sage-green shopfront add a slice of contemporary cool to Alsager's high street. Yet this isn't style over substance as, when designing the cafe, the couple's aim was to create a comfortable community space that also offered caffeination and connection.

'The thing that makes us happiest is seeing our customers – young and old – interacting and enjoying what we create,' says Alex.

TIP LOOK OUT FOR REGULAR CRAFT WORKSHOPS AND EVENTS FOR BOTH ADULTS AND KIDS

Cornwall's Origin Coffee was the roastery of choice when Home opened and is still used for the house espresso, but the team have recently roadtested coffees from Harmony in York and Kickback in Pott Shrigley and have plans to feature more regional roasteries. Espresso and batch brew are the menu stalwarts, though if you ask nicely the barista might whip out the AeroPress or V60.

Coffee is paired with a curation of locally baked savouries, pastries and cakes, which includes the very popular cardamom knots and pastel de nata.

Established
2022

Key roaster
Origin Coffee
Roasters

Brewing method
Espresso,
AeroPress, V60,
batch brew

Machine
La Marzocco
Linea Classic

Grinder
Mythos One,
Mahlkonig EK43

Opening hours
Mon-Sat
8am–4pm
Sun
10am–3pm

REUSABLES
ACCEPTED

WIFI

DOGS
WELCOME

BUY BEANS
IN STORE

GREATER
MANCHESTER
& CHESHIRE
ROASTERIES

45 SWAN SONG COFFEE ROASTERS

Unit 4 Regents Trading Estate, Oldfield Road, Salford, Greater Manchester, M5 4DE

swansong.coffee | 07920 043134

swansongcoffeeroasters

The quality of coffee shops and roasteries in and around Manchester has propelled the city to the upper echelons of the UK speciality scene. And this one-man Salford roastery – founded by former SCA trainer and UK Brewers Cup medallist Josh Wilson – is a shining example of the incredible indies putting the region on the map.

Josh only works with seasonal single-origin speciality beans, and his growing Swan Song collection includes chocolatey Brazilians, fruity Colombians, floral Ethiopians and competition-grade coffees. As the UK representative and official technician for Stronghold Technology, Josh has a duo of *'the world's premier electric smart roasters'* at his disposal and opens up the roastery (by appointment) to those who want to roadtest the kit.

'THIS ONE-MAN SALFORD ROASTERY IS A SHINING EXAMPLE OF THE INCREDIBLE INDIES PUTTING THE REGION ON THE MAP'

Sustainability is a key consideration and Josh uses a smoke-filter system to capture 99.7 per cent of his roasting emissions, while the roastery's other carbon outputs are offset by native tree planting at his family's rare-breed sheep farm in Ayrshire (in 2023, Josh and his mum planted more than 150 trees and plants).

While roasting coffee is the main focus, Josh also hosts weekly workshops where budding baristas can hone their skills via personalised tuition.

Established
2018

Roaster make and size
Stronghold Technology S9X 8kg, Stronghold Technology S7Pro 1kg

OPEN BY INVITE

COFFEE COURSES

BUY BEANS ONLINE

BUY BEANS IN STORE

46 DJANGO COFFEE CO.

Unit 5, 58–60 Higher Ardwick, Manchester, M12 6DA

djangocoffeeco.com | 01617 061457

f *djangocoffeeco* ⊙ *djangocoffeeco*

At the heart of Django Coffee Co. is a forensic focus on the origins of its coffee as well as establishing direct trade with farmers across the world. The roasting crew are uber conscientious about buying only the very best speciality beans, so every lot is ethically sourced and 100 per cent traceable.

'We believe sustainability is hugely important in the production of quality coffee,' says owner Ste Paweleck. 'We want to minimise our carbon footprint and ensure each stage of the coffee chain – from harvesting to roasting – is carried out with the kind of knowledge and understanding that does justice to everyone involved.'

'THE ROASTING CREW ARE UBER CONSCIENTIOUS ABOUT BUYING ONLY THE BEST SPECIALITY BEANS'

This year, Ste hopes to travel to El Salvador to forge relationships with new producers and to Uganda to catch up with some of Django's long-term partners. Back home, the team have invested in a larger roaster to keep up with demand and introduced carbon-neutral recyclable packaging. Plans are also afoot to open an on-site coffee shop in autumn 2023.

Established
2016

Roaster make and size
Giesen W15A 15kg,
Giesen W6A 6kg

OPEN BY INVITE

BUY BEANS ONLINE

BUY BEANS IN STORE

47 KICKBACK COFFEE

Unit 3 The Old Brickworks, Pott Shrigley, Cheshire, SK10 5RX

kickbackcoffee.co.uk | 01625 409616

f *kickbackcoffeeuk* @ *kickbackcoffee*

The spirit of adventure is as strong as the scent of roasting beans at this indie roastery, thanks to an outdoorsy vibe that's a natural by-product of building a business in the heart of the Peak District.

Following a visit to a roastery in Nottingham, Kickback owner Alex Shaw was hooked on the idea of roasting coffee and kicked off his speciality journey by cooking up beans in a popcorn machine. Ten years later, the dream of making a proper business out of his passion became a reality when Alex opened Kickback's roastery-cafe at The Old Brickworks in Cheshire – two Giesens taking over roasting duties from the novelty kitchen appliance.

'THE SPIRIT OF ADVENTURE IS AS STRONG AS THE SCENT OF ROASTING BEANS'

Kickback's signature washed blend The Explorer (a beautifully balanced fusion of nutty Nicaraguan and smooth Colombian beans, with a dash of Ethiopian beans for raisin sweetness) is perfect for those looking for a caffeine boost to fuel outdoor escapades.

The crew's most recent quest has been to reduce the roastery's carbon footprint, which has resulted in local coffee drops being delivered by Kickback's Urban Arrow e-cargo bike.

Established
2017

Roaster make and size
Giesen W30 30kg,
Giesen W15 15kg

CAFE ON SITE

OPEN TO THE PUBLIC

BUY BEANS ONLINE

BUY BEANS IN STORE

POTT SHRIGLEY

90

48 GINGER MONKEY COFFEE ROASTERS

31 Christleton Road, Boughton, Chester, Cheshire, CH3 5UF

gingermonkeyroasters.com | 01244 350894

f *gingermonkeyno31* ⊙ *gingermonkey_no31*

This family-run roastery is operated by Cal and Hayley Hawthorne, who named their flourishing coffee empire in honour of Cal's copper hair and their three cheeky offspring.

The duo began their speciality journey in 2020 when they opened the Ginger Monkey cafe in Boughton. After a successful first year in business, they upped the ante and started roasting their own coffee too.

Cal takes the lead as head roaster: sourcing, sampling and roasting every batch on an electric Aillio Bullet (which he plans to upgrade soon). Hayley's role is a mash-up of marketing, packaging, customer service and design. Together, they've created a roastery fuelled by creativity and an ambition to serve and sell exceptional beans to like-minded coffee lovers.

'THE CHINESE BEANS ARE ROASTED SLIGHTLY DARKER, BUT DON'T LET THAT DETER YOU'

Visit the roastery's cafe to sample customer favourite China Kaku. The washed Chinese beans are roasted slightly darker than other GM roasts but don't let that deter you. Cal says: *'The longer roasting time enhances the body and sweetness, something that's usually lost in a darker roast, but in Kaku results in a clean, juicy coffee with tasting notes of Granny Smith, lime rind and chocolate.'*

Established
2021

Roaster make and size
Aillio Bullet 1kg

CAFE ON SITE

OPEN TO THE PUBLIC

BUY BEANS ONLINE

BUY BEANS IN STORE

● CAFES

Middlesbroug

Darlington

A19

North Yor
Nationc

A19

53

A1(M)

54

Easingwolc

Nidderdale
AONB

55

56

85

A59

Skipton

57

58

Harrogate

Ilkley

59

Wetherby

80

86

78

LEEDS

70

City
map
see
over

68

79

71

69

73

72

Wakefield

M18

Huddersfield

M62

A1

87

M1

Barnsley

88

81

Donc

MANCHESTER

89

91

90

LIVERPOOL

SHEFFIELD

74

Peak District
National Park

75

82

76

77

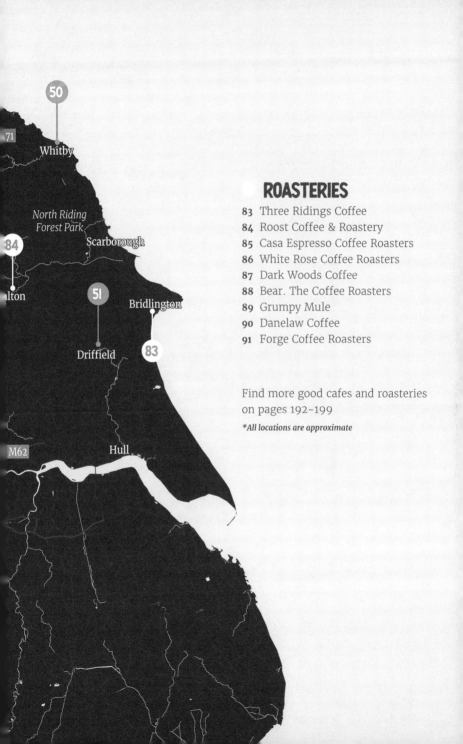

ROASTERIES

83 Three Ridings Coffee
84 Roost Coffee & Roastery
85 Casa Espresso Coffee Roasters
86 White Rose Coffee Roasters
87 Dark Woods Coffee
88 Bear. The Coffee Roasters
89 Grumpy Mule
90 Danelaw Coffee
91 Forge Coffee Roasters

Find more good cafes and roasteries on pages 192–199

All locations are approximate

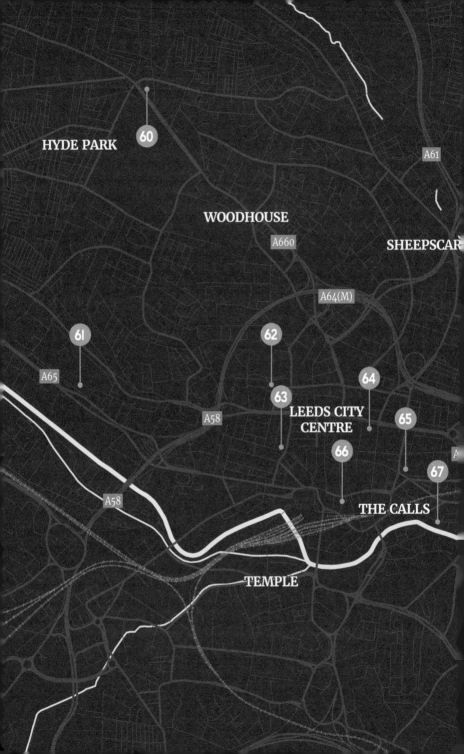

LEEDS

● CAFES

Find more good cafes and roasteries on pages 192–199

All locations are approximate

49 HEADLAND ESPRESSO

Coast Road, Redcar, Cleveland, North Yorkshire, TS10 3NN

07815 290408

f headlandespresso ⊙ headlandespresso

This espresso bar in a converted van proves you don't need bags of space to produce top-notch speciality coffee.

Barista and founder Antony Wright crafts an impressive range of drinks from his modest mobile brew bar, offering three espresso options (one for black, one for milk and a decaf) plus a filter roast that can be brewed as V60 or AeroPress.

TIP DON'T HAVE A REUSABLE? PICK UP A CIRCULAR&CO. CUP MADE FROM SINGLE-USE CUPS

This coffee shop may be on four wheels, but you'll almost always find it at Coast Road car park – whatever the weather. Overlooking the Stray (or with the hatch facing the other way during wild weather), it's the perfect place to pick up a coffee before taking a stroll along the sand.

A selection of bakes, brownies and flapjacks will fuel wanderings but those looking for something more substantial should finish their walk at sister venue Base Pizzeria & Bar in Marske-by-the-Sea. It's ace for Neapolitan-style pizza and craft beer.

Established
2021

Key roaster
Jaunty Goat

Brewing method
Espresso, V60, AeroPress

Machine
Wega Polaris

Grinder
Eureka, Macap × 2

Opening hours
Tue–Sat
8am–2pm
(seasonal opening hours)

REUSABLES ACCEPTED | BIKE FRIENDLY | DOGS WELCOME | BUY BEANS IN STORE | OUTDOOR SEATING

50 MR COOPER'S COFFEE HOUSE

72 Church Street, Whitby, North Yorkshire, YO22 4AS

01947 899904

f mrcooperswhitby ⊚ mrcooperscoffeehouse

There's little use trying to ignore (and resist) the sweet treats at this family-run coffee house as the packed-to-bursting cake haberdashery doubles as the bar from which you order coffee.

Espresso is the perfect partner to a buttery bake and the cracking Granary Blend from Rounton roastery in Northallerton delivers deliciously smooth and complementary chocolate-caramel notes. It's great black or with milk, and every cup is served with a mini Jammie Dodger.

TIP BROWSE THE IN-STORE COLLECTION OF PRINTS, BREWING KITS, TEES AND REUSABLE CUPS

A regular guest spot extends the coffee options further, with interesting roasts from highly reputable roasteries such as Girls Who Grind, The Good Coffee Cartel and Hard Lines. Guest roasts are available as batch brew, V60 and cold brew.

If something savoury is needed to counter your sweet carb-fest, we recommend exploring the seasonal bagel menu. The line-up showcases creatively off-piste fillings such as onion bhaji, mango chutney, pickled red onions, coconut and mint raita with poppadoms, alongside classics including pastrami with emmental and sauerkraut. Vibrant salads, soups and grain bowls also feature and all dishes can be boxed up to take away.

Established
2018

Key roaster
Rounton Coffee Roasters

Brewing method
Espresso, V60, batch brew, cold brew

Machine
Victoria Arduino Eagle One

Grinder
Mazzer Super Jolly, Macap

Opening hours
Mon–Sat
9am–5pm
Sun
9am–4pm

WHITBY

REUSABLES ACCEPTED   WIFI   DOGS WELCOME   BUY BEANS IN STORE   OUTDOOR SEATING

51 KINSHIP

97 Middle Street South, Driffield, East Yorkshire, YO25 6QE

kinshipcoffee.co.uk

f kinship.driffield **☉** kinship.coffee

The diminutive size of this market town coffee shop doesn't stop its founder from having big ambitions for its role in the local community.

When Tom Watson established Kinship in the centre of Driffield in September 2021, he chose a name that would reflect his aspiration to create a space where people from all walks of life could convene and connect. *'People often say they not only come for coffee but also to socialise,'* he says. *'They feel comfortable speaking to strangers here, which they wouldn't in other settings.'*

`TIP` IN SUMMER, ASK FOR AN AFFOGATO MADE WITH NORTHERN BLOC ICE CREAM

Being the only speciality venue within a 15-mile radius means that this small space is often humming with activity. Coffee fans make the trip to sample the house roast, George Street from Kiss the Hippo, as well as guest beans from Square Mile. For special events such as Yorkshire Day, Tom collaborates with local roastery Three Ridings to create limited-edition espressos.

After a successful first year in business, Kinship ended 2022 with a kit upgrade and welcomed a spanking new VA Eagle One machine and an extra Mahlkonig grinder to the set-up.

Established
2021

Key roaster
Kiss the Hippo

Brewing method
Espresso, V60, batch filter, cold brew

Machine
Victoria Arduino Eagle One

Grinder
Mahlkonig E65S GbW x 2

Opening hours
Mon–Fri
8am–4pm
Sat
8am–2.30pm

WIFI BIKE FRIENDLY DOGS WELCOME BUY BEANS IN STORE OUTDOOR SEATING

DRIFFIELD

52 RISE - YORK

44 Fossgate, York, North Yorkshire, YO1 9TF

risebrunch.co.uk

f risebrunch *⊙ risebrunch*

Fossgate in the heart of York has been a busy hub of shops and eateries for centuries, so when the Rise team were searching for a site in the city for their social-cafe concept, joining the street's community of indies was a no-brainer.

They snapped up a roomy spot with bags of natural light and created an outpost to mirror their original cafe in Preston, which focuses on antipodean-style brunch dishes and espresso-based coffee from London's Ozone. The aesthetic is contemporary, fun and geared up for the grid with a pastel-pink palette, bleached wood and hanging houseplants.

TIP MAKE A WEEKEND TRIP FOR THE BILL OF BRUNCH SPECIALS

The all-day menu is built around brunch classics, such as eggs benedict, turkish eggs and smoothie bowls, but elevated by the Rise chefs. Seasonal line-ups keep the offering fresh – ask the team for their current faves and recommendations.

In summer, street seating hosts alfresco brunchers keen to soak up the Yorkshire sunshine. And if you can't bag a table, pick up an iced coffee or homemade smoothie to-go and take a stroll around the city walls.

Established
2022

Key roaster
Ozone Coffee

Brewing method
Espresso, cold brew

Machine
La Marzocco
Linea PB

Grinder
Mazzer Kold S

Opening hours
Mon-Fri
8am-5pm
Sat-Sun
9am-5pm

REUSABLES ACCEPTED   WIFI   BIKE FRIENDLY   BUY BEANS IN STORE   OUTDOOR SEATING

53 BREW BAR HARROGATE

41 St Winifred's Avenue, Harrogate, North Yorkshire, HG2 8LT

brewbarharrogate.co.uk | 07875 701748

f *43brewbarharrogate* ⊙ *brewbarharrogate*

Community is at the core of this Harrogate coffee shop. From the pay-it-forward scheme providing free drinks for NHS workers to the Community Table where solo visitors can chat with other coffee sippers, connectivity is encouraged.

There are quiet corners where new mums can feed their babies, roomy tables with charging points for freelancers looking to escape the spare room and phone chargers available for anyone running out of juice. *'We're always trying to evolve to provide the best possible experience for our customers,'* says founder Simon Somerville-Frost.

TIP A REUSABLE-CUP LOYALTY SCHEME REWARDS WASTE-CONSCIOUS CUSTOMERS WITH THEIR FIFTH DRINK FREE

Fuelling this community spirit is ethically sourced, speciality-grade coffee from two Northern roasting powerhouses. County Durham's Lonton Coffee Co supplies the signature Brew Bar house coffee – a mix of Brazilian, Indonesian and Central American beans – while two blends (Deer Hill and Arboretum) from Dark Woods in Huddersfield provide backup.

Homemade artisan bakes take inspiration from the corner shop and include the likes of KitKat cookie caramel slice, Nutella cookie pie, and Biscoff and Gold Bar rocky road.

Established
2018

Key roaster
Lonton Coffee Co

Brewing method
Espresso

Machine
La Spaziale S5

Grinder
Mahlkonig E65S GbW

Opening hours
Mon
8am–2.30pm
Tue–Sat
8am–4pm

REUSABLES ACCEPTED   WIFI   BIKE FRIENDLY   DOGS WELCOME   BUY BEANS IN STORE   OUTDOOR SEATING

54 STARLING

47 Oxford Street, Harrogate, North Yorkshire, HG1 1PW

starlinghgte.co.uk | 01423 531310

f *starlinghgte* ⊚ *starlinghgte*

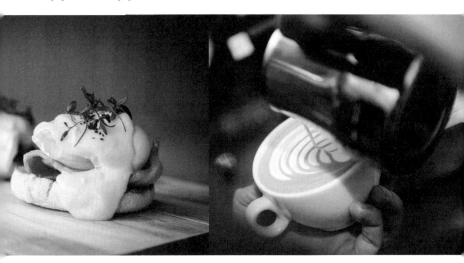

Thanks to its daytime brunches, speciality coffee, craft beers and light bites, this morning-to-evening cafe-bar keeps Harrogate carefully caffeinated and very well fed.

The first cup of the day is the most important and Starling's wake-up brews don't disappoint: Dark Woods' stellar Under Milk Wood forms the basis of all the silky espresso drinks, while single-origin roasts from Origin and Caravan are utilised in V60s and batch brew.

Pair your morning coffee with a classic brunch plate (available until 2.30pm, so a late lie-in is possible) such as stacked American pancakes, a bacon sarnie or avo-topped sourdough. Other treats include Starling stalwart the three-egg slider (eggs benny, florentine and royale on one plate) and a Med meatball bake comprising homemade meatballs, feta, spinach, olives, tomato, mozzarella and sourdough.

TIP PLANNING AN EVENT OR WORKSHOP? THE CAFE'S EVENT SPACE, THE BARN, IS BOOKABLE

As brunch comes to a close, the bar tends to fill with visitors drooling over the pizza and light bites menu and checking out what's cold and on draft. Vegans don't miss out either, thanks to a large selection of plant-based pizzas and pints.

Established
2017

Key roaster
Dark Woods Coffee

Brewing method
Espresso,
V60, batch brew

Machine
La Marzocco Linea

Grinder
Mahlkonig E65S,
Mahlkonig EK43

Opening hours
Mon-Wed
9am-10pm
Thu-Sat
9am-11pm
Sun
10am-10pm

REUSABLES ACCEPTED · WIFI · BIKE FRIENDLY · DOGS WELCOME · BUY BEANS IN STORE · COFFEE COURSES · OUTDOOR SEATING

55 BEAN LOVED

17 Otley Street, Skipton, North Yorkshire, BD23 1DY

beanloved.co.uk | 01756 791534

f beanlovedskipton *⊙ beanloved*

Recently crowned Yorkshire's Coffee Shop of the Year in the Corporate Livewire Prestige Awards, this long-standing fave isn't resting on its laurels.

Bean Loved's secret to over 15 years of success is getting the basics right – which includes serving really good coffee. Landscape, the bespoke house blend from Dark Woods in Huddersfield, turns first-time visitors into adoring regulars thanks to its subtle complexity and crowd-pleasingly sweet finish. The Swiss Water Decaf – also roasted by DWC – receives equally rave reviews.

TIP BROWSE THE RETAIL SHELVES STOCKED WITH SINGLE-ORIGIN BEANS FROM HERO ROASTERIES

Another string to the cafe's bow is its unique brunch and lunch offering. The talented crew of chefs make everything in-house and regularly update the menu to include fresh seasonal produce. A new fried-chicken focaccia with pickled vegetables and sweet chilli jam (made using a top-secret recipe) is the latest must-try dish on the line-up.

An easy-going atmosphere and friendly baristas are the cherry on top of the award-winning Bean Loved experience.

Established
2007

Key roaster
Dark Woods Coffee

Brewing method
Espresso

Machine
La Marzocco KB90

Grinder
Mahlkonig E80,
Mahlkonig E65S

Opening hours
Mon–Fri
8am–3pm
Sat
8am–4pm
Sun
9am–3pm

REUSABLES ACCEPTED   WIFI   BIKE FRIENDLY   BUY BEANS IN STORE   OUTDOOR SEATING

56 THE CLUBHOUSE - SKIPTON

18 Newmarket Street, Skipton, North Yorkshire, BD23 2HR

theclubhousecc.co.uk | 01756 793124

f theclubhousecc ⊙ theclubhousecoffee

The Clubhouse is the only cafe in Skipton that serves own-roasted coffee, so owner Kane Pulford-Roberts and team are pretty proud of themselves. Kane sources beans from across the globe, which he roasts in batches at the cafe's micro-roastery.

Those looking to taste test the shifting collection of flavour-popping beans should drop into the Newmarket Street coffee house to sample the latest single origin as a whistle-clean V60, try the house blend as espresso, or investigate something fruity via batch brew.

TIP DON'T LEAVE WITHOUT GIVING GEORGE, THE CLUBHOUSE'S RESIDENT POOCH, SOME LOVE

The cafe is the natural home of local speciality coffee enthusiasts, but it's also a popular hangout for Skipton's cycling community. A jersey signed by Bradley Wiggins and the bike he rode in the Tour de Yorkshire 2016 are proudly displayed on the wall.

Whether you're making a cycling pit stop or taking a coffee break from work, toast toppings such as the peanut butter, banana, seeds and honey combo are guaranteed to power up the rest of your day. Kane and crew are conscious of the rising cost of living so have also introduced specials such as a flat white and bacon sarnie for £6.

Established
2018

Key roaster
The Clubhouse

Brewing method
Espresso, V60,
AeroPress,
batch brew

Machine
La Marzocco
Linea Classic

Grinder
Nuova Simonelli

Opening hours
Tue-Sat
8.30am-4pm
Sun
10am-3pm

SKIPTON

WIFI | BIKE FRIENDLY | DOGS WELCOME | BUY BEANS IN STORE | OUTDOOR SEATING

57 TAMBOURINE COFFEE

38 Bingley Road, Saltaire, West Yorkshire, BD18 4RU

tambourinecoffee.co.uk

☉ *tambourinecoffee*

When taking over a much-loved coffee shop in a small village, the key to success is to make your own mark while providing consistency for the regulars. Ailsa and Tom Pater nailed it when they took over Tambourine in April 2022, giving the space a fresh lick of paint, pivoting the food offering towards a seasonal organic menu and ensuring the quality of the coffee remained tip-top.

Ailsa rustles up a daily changing line-up of dishes, which customers can eat in or take away. Expect the likes of seasonal soups, salads, quiches and curries, as well as springy focaccia sandwiches stacked with kale pesto and sheep's cheese or beetroot hummus and sprouts. It's proper wholesome fodder that will leave you feeling well nourished rather than sleepily sluggish.

TIP CHECK INSTAGRAM FOR NEWS OF POP-UP PLANT-BASED SUPPER CLUBS

North Star provides the bulk of the coffee beans used at Tambourine, bolstered by a regular rotation of guest coffees from Red Bank, Carringtons, Danelaw and Maude – among others. Espresso shots are topped with creamy organic milk from Yorkshire's Acorn Dairy, which creates the perfect partner for a homemade sticky cinnamon bun.

Established
2017

Key roaster
North Star
Coffee Roasters

Brewing method
Espresso, filter

Machine
La Marzocco
Linea Classic

Grinder
Mahlkonig E65S,
Mahlkonig EK43

Opening hours
Mon–Sat
8am–4pm
Sun
9am–3pm

REUSABLES ACCEPTED   WIFI   BIKE FRIENDLY   DOGS WELCOME   BUY BEANS IN STORE   OUTDOOR SEATING

58 FIKA NORTH

94 Otley Road, Far Headingley, Leeds, West Yorkshire, LS6 4BA

fikanorth.co.uk | 01138 243489

f fikanorthcoffee *◎ fikanorth*

Inspired by our friends in Sweden and the creative spirit of Yorkshire' is how head barista Ollie Gorman describes this popular coffee shop and wine bar in Far Headingley.

Fika North's chilled pace and thoughtful approach is no doubt influenced by Ollie's experience living in Stockholm and the rest of the team's trips to the Scandinavian coast to visit friends. The relaxed set-up and emphasis on connection encourages visitors to slow down and enjoy the good things in life (in this case, quality coffee and artisan cinnamon buns).

TIP VISIT FIKA NORTH'S NEW NATURAL-WINE SHOP AND DELI, BOTTLE CHOP, UP THE ROAD

Locally roasted coffee from Casa, freshly ground by a new duo of Mahlkonig grinders, is savoured as espresso-based pours. The baristas have gone slightly 'batch-brew crazy' (their words, not ours) and switch up the guest roasteries every week, so there's always something new and exciting to sample.

Massive toasted bagels are the big-hitters on the savoury menu and feature delish fillings such as halloumi, hash browns, hollandaise and chives. For something sweeter, check out the tempting selection of flaky pastries.

Established
2019

Key roaster
Casa Espresso
Coffee Roasters

Brewing method
Espresso,
batch brew

Machine
La Marzocco
Linea PB AV

Grinder
Mahlkonig EK43,
Mahlkonig E65
GbW

Opening hours
Mon–Fri
8am–5pm
Sat–Sun
9am–5pm

LEEDS

REUSABLES ACCEPTED WIFI BIKE FRIENDLY DOGS WELCOME BUY BEANS IN STORE OUTDOOR SEATING

59 BOWERY

54 Otley Road, Headingley, Leeds, West Yorkshire, LS6 2AL

thebowery.org | 01132 242284

f boweryleeds *ⓞ boweryleeds*

A coffee shop, workspace and creative hub rolled into one, Bowery is a mecca of all things beautifully crafted – from a perfectly poured Allpress espresso to an abstract art exhibition.

The speciality coffee is curated by head barista Ged Togher, who not only dispatches exceptional espresso and filter coffee but also shares his bean boffinry with budding baristas at the regular Bowery Coffee School workshops.

TIP CHECK THE WEBSITE FOR UPCOMING ART, MUSIC, WRITING AND COFFEE WORKSHOPS

Pair your caffeine buzz with a sugar hit from the cafe's array of alluring bakes, and then settle down to immerse yourself in the creative ambience. For something more substantial, a line-up of hearty toasted sandwiches and vibrant salads delivers in spades.

Bowery is also home to a shop and gallery, and hosts workshops, events and parties. It's freelancer friendly too, so feel welcome to take your laptop up to the gallery space and blast through your emails as you work through the coffee menu.

Established
2008

Key roaster
Allpress Espresso

Brewing method
Espresso, filter

Machine
La Marzocco
Linea Classic

Grinder
Mazzer Super Jolly

Opening hours
Mon–Sun
9am–5pm

REUSABLES ACCEPTED   WIFI   BIKE FRIENDLY   BUY BEANS IN STORE   COFFEE COURSES   OUTDOOR SEATING

60 COFFEE ON THE CRESCENT

2 The Crescent, Hyde Park, Leeds, West Yorkshire, LS6 2NW

coffeeonthecrescent.co.uk | 01132 160380

f coffeeonthecrescentleeds *⊙ coffeeonthecrescent*

Speciality fans visiting the Hyde Park area of Leeds should check out Coffee on the Crescent, not because it's the brainchild of former pro cricketer Timothy Linley but because it's a cool hangout for those interested in pushing the coffee boat out.

A rotating line-up of guest roasts means there's always something delicious from the likes of North Star, Echelon or Dark Woods to seduce the palate. And, should you find yourself torn between two tempting options, there's an opportunity to take a mini tasting flight and sample both brews to compare flavour profiles. The team take pride in having cupped every coffee before it's served – or sold in bags – so will always share recommendations.

TIP BUY A BAG OF LIMITED-EDITION COFFEE ON YOUR WAY OUT

On the food front, patisserie pleasures such as almond croissants, cinnamon buns and a rotation of brownies and cakes complement stalwart cafe dishes like soup, sandwiches and savouries.

A tangible love of good coffee and food spills over into community spirit too: in the past two years the team have raised more than £5,000 for a local foodbank and rejuvenated a piece of wasteland into a beautiful spot to enjoy coffee alfresco, called The Birdcage.

Established
2017

Key roaster
Echelon Coffee Roasters

Brewing method
Espresso, filter

Machine
La Marzocco Linea AV

Grinder
Fiorenzato F64

Opening hours
Mon–Sat
8.30am–4.30pm
Sun
9am–4.30pm

REUSABLES ACCEPTED

DOGS WELCOME

BUY BEANS IN STORE

OUTDOOR SEATING

LEEDS

61 ARCHIVE

94 Kirkstall Road, Leeds, West Yorkshire, LS3 1HD

archiveleeds.co.uk | 07444 710139

f archiveleeds *⊚ archiveleeds*

It's only natural that this coffee shop and events space within Prime Studios – one of the largest independent film and television studios in the north of England – has found fame for its crowd-pleasing food. While star-studded dramas are being filmed in the surrounding studios, Archive turns out its own works of art in the form of rosetta-adorned lattes and pap-worthy brunch and lunch plates.

TIP ENJOY YOUR ORDER ALFRESCO IN THE NEW HEATED OUTDOOR SEATING AREA

The exciting menu of edibles features classic cafe fare like smashed avo on toast and eggs benny, alongside creative dishes such as kedgeree risotto (curry-spiced rice with smoked haddock, lime, coriander and poached eggs).

On the coffee front, star billing goes to the house espresso from Casa which is fabulous served as a velvety flat white. Alternatively, choose from a supporting cast of guest pourovers from the likes of Hard Lines, Outpost and Square Mile.

Local? Check out Archive's regular events, which range from film screenings and vintage clothing pop-ups to live music and board-game nights.

Established
2019

Key roaster
Casa Espresso
Coffee Roasters

Brewing method
Espresso,
cold brew,
pourover,
batch brew

Machine
Synesso MVP Hydra

Grinder
Slingshot C68

Opening hours
Mon
8.30am–3pm
Tue, Fri
8.30am–4pm
Wed–Thu
8.30am–9pm
Sat–Sun
10am–4pm

REUSABLES ACCEPTED · WIFI · BIKE FRIENDLY · DOGS WELCOME · BUY BEANS IN STORE · COFFEE COURSES · OUTDOOR SEATING

62 STAGE ESPRESSO & BREW BAR

41 Great George Street, Leeds, West Yorkshire, LS1 3BB

stagecoffee.com | 07527 534983

f stagecoffee ⓞ *stagecoffeeleeds*

Stage debuted on the Leeds coffee scene in 2017 and has been putting in a star performance ever since.

Coming from a team who don't do things by halves, the coffee garners rave reviews for everything from bean sourcing to brew style and service. Single-estate beans from a bill of UK roasteries take centre stage in the La Marzocco or showcased as batch brew, Kalita Wave or Clever Dripper.

TIP PICKING UP BEANS AND KIT TO BREW AT HOME? ASK THE BARISTAS FOR THEIR PREP TIPS

A banging brunch menu and counter laden with locally made cakes form a supporting cast to the speciality coffee. Served all day, the pleasingly pared-back food line-up features the likes of sweetcorn fritters with halloumi and pesto, and kasundi baked eggs.

Following a post-lockdown refurb, Stage has expanded its repertoire and now hosts special events and Sofar Sounds music sessions. Local craft beers, wines, artisan soft drinks and late-night espressos fuel the after-hours fun.

Established
2017

Key roaster
Multiple roasteries

Brewing method
Espresso,
Kalita Wave,
Clever Dripper,
batch brew

Machine
La Marzocco GB5 S

Grinder
Victoria Arduino
Mythos One,
Mahlkonig EK43

Opening hours
Mon-Fri
8.30am-3.30pm

REUSABLES ACCEPTED WIFI DOGS WELCOME BUY BEANS IN STORE

63 THE CLUBHOUSE - LEEDS

8a St Paul's Street, Leeds, West Yorkshire, LS1 2LE

theclubhousecc.co.uk | 01132 442519

theclubhouseleeds *theclubhouseleeds*

Leeds isn't short of fantastic places to down a decent brew, but this newbie to the city is definitely worth a spot on your coffee hit-list.

It may be a recent addition to Leeds but The Clubhouse is no fresher to the coffee scene. Since it opened in 2018, the original cafe in Skipton has become a speciality hub in the North Yorkshire town and is so popular that owner Kane Pulford-Roberts felt confident in opening this sister site. Head to St Paul's Street to experience the cafe's house-roasted coffee, freshly prepped food and cheerful charm.

TIP NEED HELP NARROWING YOUR SANDWICH CHOICE? THE DIRTY REUBEN IS TOP NOTCH

Beans fresh from The Clubhouse micro-roastery are served as espresso, V60 and batch, and make a perfect partner to the epic brunch and lunch plates. Everything is made to order in the open-plan kitchen and the current house fave is the The Clubhouse Benedict, in which sticky honey brisket, poached eggs and sriracha hollandaise are piled on potato hash.

Visiting at the start of the week? Ask about Industry Mondays, which could earn you a sweet ten per cent discount.

Established
2022

Key roaster
The Clubhouse

Brewing method
Espresso, V60, batch brew

Machine
La Marzocco Linea Classic

Grinder
Quamar Q13E

Opening hours
Mon-Fri
7am-4pm

LEEDS

REUSABLES ACCEPTED | WIFI | BIKE FRIENDLY | DOGS WELCOME | BUY BEANS IN STORE | COFFEE COURSES

64 KAPOW COFFEE - THORNTON'S ARCADE

15 Thornton's Arcade, Leeds, West Yorkshire, LS1 6LQ

kapowcoffee.co.uk

f *kapowcoffee* © *kapowcoffee*

This colourful comic-book-inspired coffee shop within Leeds' Thornton's Arcade is home to some of the city's most experienced baristas.

The team's fanaticism for all things speciality is immediately obvious from their comprehensive retail offering that's one of the best in Yorkshire. Beans from Kawa, Friedhats, Assembly, New Ground and many more regularly bless the shelves. A plethora of brewing equipment is also available to help visitors make the most of their pick of the beans on sale, while clued-up baristas are on hand with brewing advice.

TIP TAKE YOUR COFFEE UPSTAIRS TO SIP WHILE SUNK IN ONE OF THE VINTAGE LEATHER ARMCHAIRS

Kapow's own custom blend of naturally processed Brazilian and Ethiopian beans – roasted by one of the Kapow team at local roastery Chipp – is the main house coffee and the crew go the extra mile to ensure every shot is spot-on. Even if you're just popping in to pick up a bag of beans, it would be madness to leave without taking a flattie for the road.

If that all sounds slightly intimidating, it shouldn't. The crew take great pride in giving a warm welcome and providing genuine and attentive hospitality.

Established
2013

Key roaster
Kapow Coffee

Brewing method
Espresso, V60, Orea, Tricolate

Machine
Sanremo Opera

Grinder
Mahlkonig E65S GbW

Opening hours
Mon-Sat
7.30am-6pm
Sun
10am-4.30pm

REUSABLES ACCEPTED | WIFI | BIKE FRIENDLY | DOGS WELCOME | BUY BEANS IN STORE | COFFEE COURSES | OUTDOOR SEATING

90% of coffee shops think they serve the best hot chocolate...

...the other 10% know they do.

www.harryshotchocolate.co.uk

65 MILES & CO COFFEE

Unit 21 Market Hall, Kirkgate Market, Leeds, West Yorkshire, LS2 7HJ

milesandcocoffee.co.uk | 07714 821523

f milesandcocoffee *milesandcocoffee*

This coffee bar within Kirkgate Market may be small but it punches well above its weight in terms of quality and commitment. Founded by barista Lee and digital-marketing expert Ellenor, Miles & Co is named after Lee's grandfather – a tribute to the man who raised him.

It's a great spot for coffee fans who like to try out new beans and discover fresh roasteries. While you can usually guarantee finding something good from Huddersfield roastery Dark Woods, Miles & Co also keeps a guest spot for the likes of Oddkin, Quarter Horse, New Ground and Chipp. Lee and Ellenor are passionate about coffee and happy to give customers the low-down on their latest roasts and the brew styles that will get the best out of them.

TIP GIVE THE GIFT OF EXCEPTIONAL COFFEE WITH A MILES & CO GIFT CARD

While the couple's bean choices meet the needs of serious coffee fans (anaerobic and single-estate coffees often feature), they don't turn up their noses at seasonal crowd-pleasers such as Biscoff lattes and festive hot chocolates.

On the counter, a small collection of locally made bakes – including cinnamon knots, pastel de nata and vegan New York-style cookies – provides a perfect match for the quality drinks and friendly vibe.

Established
2021

Key roaster
Dark Woods Coffee

Brewing method
Espresso, batch brew, Kalita Wave

Machine
La Marzocco Linea Classic

Grinder
Anfim Pratica

Opening hours
Mon–Fri
8am–4.30pm
Sat
9am–5pm

REUSABLES ACCEPTED   WIFI   DOGS WELCOME   BUY BEANS IN STORE   COFFEE COURSES

66 LAYNES ESPRESSO

16 New Station Street, Leeds, West Yorkshire, LS1 5DL

laynesespresso.co.uk | 07828 823189

f laynesespresso *@ laynesespresso*

Founder Dave Olejnik has continued to build on Laynes' roaring success this year, further extending the venue on New Station Street to accommodate more guests and expand the kitchen and its offering.

What started out in 2011 as a humble espresso bar near Leeds train station has become a speciality institution in the city. In 2018, Dave took over the neighbouring unit and expanded the space to keep up with demand. Then, in 2022, he established a sister bakery in Armley to stock the original shop with homemade pastries, cakes and sourdough.

TIP THERE'S ALWAYS A GUEST COFFEE OR TWO AVAILABLE AS BATCH OR POUROVER

While Laynes now attracts as many visitors for its all-day brunch plates as its espresso, the focus on serving the finest speciality coffee hasn't wavered. Its skilled baristas are known for pouring some of the best flat whites in the city.

If you can score a table, stick around for something to eat and feast on the likes of polenta with eggs and chorizo, and eggy brioche with bacon, cream cheese, chives and maple syrup.

Established
2011

Key roaster
Square Mile
Coffee Roasters

Brewing method
Espresso, pourover, batch brew

Machine
Synesso MVP

Grinder
Mahlkonig E80
Supreme

Opening hours
Mon–Fri
7.30am–3pm
Sat
8am–6pm
Sun
9am–4pm

REUSABLES
ACCEPTED

WIFI

DOGS
WELCOME

BUY BEANS
IN STORE

OUTDOOR
SEATING

67 KAPOW COFFEE - THE CALLS

46 The Calls, Leeds, West Yorkshire, LS2 7EY

kapowcoffee.co.uk

f *kapowcoffee* ⓘ *kapowcoffee*

Tucked away beside the River Aire and located a few doors down from Kapow's original coffee shop, this neighbourhood hangout offers respite from the city centre crowds. The coffee offering replicates that of its sister site in Thornton's Arcade and features Kapow's own espresso (notes of cocoa, hazelnut and dried fruit), which sits back-to-back with single-origin batch options from the house roastery and guest roasteries from across the UK.

Fresh sandwiches and pastries to pair with the drinks are always in plentiful supply, while the retail shelves are stacked with interesting beans from international roasters of note.

TIP GRAB A SEAT OUTSIDE AND SOAK UP THE ATMOSPHERE OF ONE OF LEEDS' OLDEST STREETS

Kapow is renowned for the hospitality of its team and being a friendly part of the local community - so much so that manager Steve prides himself on remembering the favourite drinks of every regular customer.

Established
2013

Key roaster
Kapow Coffee

Brewing method
Espresso, V60, filter, AeroPress, cold brew

Machine
Sanremo F18

Grinder
Victoria Arduino Mythos One

Opening hours
Mon-Fri
7.30am-5pm
Sat-Sun
9am-5pm

REUSABLES
ACCEPTED

WIFI

BIKE
FRIENDLY

DOGS
WELCOME

BUY BEANS
IN STORE

OUTDOOR
SEATING

68 GOOD MOOD

24 Commercial Street, Halifax, West Yorkshire, HX1 1TA

goodmoodbar.co.uk

🄾 *goodmoodhfx*

Halifax got a dose of London coffee culture when former Taylor St barista Ross Thomas established this speciality shop in 2020. Despite starting a business in one of the most challenging years for indies, Ross and the Good Mood crew have created a thriving hub and won over the espresso-loving, craft-beer-chugging locals.

Using experience gained from the pioneering London cafe group, Ross trains all the Good Mood baristas to ensure every cup is on point. Espresso is the main focus and Campbell & Syme supplies an extensive range of beans on which the baristas work their magic. Those who prefer filter will find V60 and batch brew options from the London roastery, plus occasional guests.

TIP CHECK OUT THE MERCH LOCKER STACKED WITH BRANDED TEES, SHOPPERS AND MORE

Visit for the coffee and then stick around for the craft beer: a good selection from local breweries is available on tap, while the fridge is stocked with eye-catching cans and bottles. Beers and natural wines are also available to go.

On the food front, a menu of Mexican favourites such as breakfast burritos, chorizo tacos and empanadas won't disappoint.

Established
2020

Key roaster
Campbell & Syme

Brewing method
Espresso, V60, batch brew

Machine
Sanremo Opera

Grinder
Victoria Arduino Mythos 2, Mahlkonig EK43 S

Opening hours
Wed–Thu
10am–10pm
Fri–Sat
10am–12am
Sun
11am–8pm

REUSABLES
ACCEPTED

WIFI

BIKE
FRIENDLY

DOGS
WELCOME

BUY BEANS
IN STORE

HALIFAX

118

69 TRIANGLE BAKEHOUSE

Commercial Mills, Oldham Road, Ripponden, West Yorkshire, HX6 4EH

trianglebakehouse.co.uk | 07902 313773

f trianglebakehouse1 © *trianglebakehouse*

Passersby can't help but be enticed by the intoxicating aromas of just-baked bread and freshly brewed coffee that flow from this popular cafe-bakery in Ripponden.

Inspired by the Swedish tradition of fika, owners Vic and Aaron Roberts decided to recreate the social concept back home in Yorkshire. The result is Triangle Bakehouse, a communal village space where locals can take a break and munch on irresistibly sticky cardamom buns and savour brews crafted with Ryburn Espresso, made in collaboration with Echelon Coffee Roasters in Leeds.

TIP PICK UP A BAG OF THE HOUSE COFFEE TO BREW AT HOME FROM THE WELL-STOCKED BAKERY SHOP

Since opening in 2018, it's become a go-to for people seeking out bakes that are good for the soul and the planet. The team craft springy sourdough using UK stoneground flour, some of which is freshly milled in-house, while a diverse range of heritage grains are sourced to create inventive loaves, including wholegrain einkorn flour from Side Oven Bakery in East Yorkshire.

Alongside the recent espresso collab with Echelon, the guest grinder hosts roasts from the likes of Dark Woods, Crankhouse, Blossom, North Star, New Ground and Origin.

Established
2018

Key roaster
Echelon Coffee Roasters

Brewing method
Espresso, V60

Machine
La Marzocco

Grinder
Anfim

Opening hours
Wed–Fri
7am–2pm
Sat
8am–2pm

BIKE
FRIENDLY

DOGS
WELCOME

OUTDOOR
SEATING

RIPPONDEN

70 COFFEEVOLUTION

8 Church Street, Huddersfield, West Yorkshire, HD1 1DD
coffeevolution.co.uk | 01484 432881
f *coffeevolution* ⓘ *coffeevolutionhuddersfield*

If 23 years at the heart of Huddersfield's coffee community doesn't cement Coffeevolution's iconic status, its recent People's Choice award for Best Coffee Shop in Huddersfield and its Good Food Awards listing among Yorkshire's top 12 coffee shops leaves no room for doubt.

The cafe's enduring reputation is owed, in part, to its friendly and knowledgeable baristas. The team not only utilise a glorious spectrum of brewing methods and interesting beans (from sister brand Bean Brothers Coffee Company and a league of guest roasteries), but also help customers achieve the same delicious results at home by offering handy tips and kit recommendations.

TIP THE TEAM SPOIL WELL-BEHAVED DOGS EVERY BIT AS MUCH AS THEY LOOK AFTER THEIR OWNERS

Coffeevolution's super-comforting food and drink menu sees regulars' favourites, like its bacon and cream cheese bagel and hot chocolate brownie with cream, joined by an expanding selection of vegetarian and vegan options.

Established
2000

Key roaster
Bean Brothers
Coffee Company

Brewing method
Espresso, V60,
Chemex, AeroPress,
syphon, cold brew

Machine
La Marzocco FB80

Grinder
Mahlkonig K30 Twin,
Mahlkonig EK43,
Anfim

Opening hours
Mon–Sat
7am–5pm
Sun
9am–4pm

REUSABLES ACCEPTED | WIFI | BIKE FRIENDLY | DOGS WELCOME | BUY BEANS IN STORE | OUTDOOR SEATING

7| ARCADE COFFEE & FOOD

9-10 Byram Arcade, Huddersfield, West Yorkshire, HD1 1ND

arcadecoffee.co.uk | 01484 511148

f arcadecoffeefood *◎ arcadecoffeefood*

Housed in a gloriously grand Victorian arcade, this Huddersfield fave attracts a steady stream of customers for its top-drawer coffee and delicious food.

It's a popular spot for recaffeination after a wander through the indie shops of Byram Arcade, the encaustic-tiled floors and atrium seating providing a pleasingly historic counterpoint to Arcade's on-trend playlist and hipster vibe.

Tuck into brunchtime classics like huevos rancheros and shakshuka, or choose from a cheerful selection of lunchtime bagels, burgers and daily specials. The line-up is updated regularly to reflect what's in season and grown locally.

TIP ARCADE'S SUPPER CLUBS BOOK UP QUICKLY SO KEEP AN EYE ON SOCIALS FOR UPCOMING DATES

On Sundays, the Arcade chefs turn their attention to the mighty roast dinner. The team are also branching out into evening events and host a regular pop-up supper club where visitors can feast on a selection of seasonally appropriate small plates.

Dark Woods Coffee, just seven miles away, roasts the beans for the cafe's reliably good house espresso. Guest roasts are available on batch brew.

Established
2017

Key roaster
Dark Woods Coffee

Brewing method
Espresso,
batch brew

Machine
La Marzocco
Linea Classic

Grinder
Anfim Pratica

Opening hours
Mon-Sat
8am-4.30pm
Sun
10am-4.30pm

REUSABLES ACCEPTED   WIFI   DOGS WELCOME   BUY BEANS IN STORE

72 ESPRESSO CORNER

11 Kirkgate, Huddersfield, West Yorkshire, HD1 1QS
espressocorner.co.uk | 01484 427325
f espressocorner *@ espressocorner*

One of the three best-rated cafes in Huddersfield, Espresso Corner is celebrated for its winning combination of quirky interiors, artisanal bites and shameless coffee geekery.

Soft music, happy chatter and the aroma of freshly ground Square Mile and Bean Brothers coffee waft across a room neatly scattered with old school desks, wooden benches and verdant plants. On entry, it's hard not to be distracted by the vintage bike hanging on the wall, but you'll soon be lured by the scents drifting from the La Marzocco machine on the counter.

TIP EMBRACE THE COFFEE GEEKERY BY TOPPING UP YOUR BEANS AND BREWING KIT

Both local and Cakesmiths bakes entice from the countertop, making it almost impossible not to relent to carby creations such as vegan sticky toffee Biscoff loaf, chocolate-orange truffle cake, and salted butterscotch and walnut cookies.

For savoury treats, look no further than the freshly crafted sandwiches made with bread from Roger's Bakery, or breakfast staples such as the classic bacon sandwich and avo on toast with feta and lime.

Established
2013

Key roaster
Square Mile
Coffee Roasters

Brewing method
Espresso, V60,
AeroPress,
syphon, Chemex

Machine
La Marzocco
Linea PB

Grinder
Mahlkonig K30
Twin, Mazzer,
Anfim

Opening hours
Mon-Fri
8am-5pm
Sat
8am-4pm

REUSABLES ACCEPTED WIFI BIKE FRIENDLY DOGS WELCOME BUY BEANS IN STORE OUTDOOR SEATING

73 ACORN & PIP

6-7 Carr Lane, Slaithwaite, Huddersfield, West Yorkshire, HD7 5AN

acornandpip.com | 01484 847968

f acornandpip | *◎ acornandpip*

In a world where it's exceptionally easy to shop online at the click of a button, Acorn & Pip has mastered the art of IRL experiential shopping. The cafe, play area and lifestyle store is the kind of place where you can shop for treasures and catch up with friends while your little ones let off steam without judgement.

The uber-family-friendly cafe was designed with the conscientious consumer in mind, so 80 per cent of the produce used in the kitchen is sourced from within eight miles. Experience it in old favourites like organic beans on sourdough or go off-piste with crumpets laden with lemon-curd cream cheese, granola, banana, coconut and wild-blossom honey. Kids will love the buttered crumpet soldiers with banana, dried apple rings and strawberry jam dip. Toasties, wraps and a counter brimming with homemade bakes complete the pleasingly simple veggie menu.

TIP DON'T LEAVE WITHOUT BROWSING THE FABULOUS SELECTION OF TOYS AND CHILDRENSWEAR

Coffee fixes are supplied via beans from local roastery Dark Woods. The house blend, Deer Hill, is an Italian-style espresso which delivers a winning flat white, while the fruity Lamplight Decaf and range of superfood smoothies and organic soft drinks provide caffeine-free thrills.

Established
2018

Key roaster
Dark Woods Coffee

Brewing method
Espresso

Machine
Sanremo

Grinder
Anfim Milano

Opening hours
Mon–Sat
9.30am–5pm
Sun
10am–4pm

REUSABLES ACCEPTED | WIFI | BIKE FRIENDLY | BUY BEANS IN STORE | OUTDOOR SEATING

HUDDERSFIELD

123

HUNDRED
HOUSE
COFFEE

SPECIALITY
COFFEE
ROASTERS

H H co

COFFEE WITH CHARACTER

74 WIRED COFFEE AND CAKE

17 Church Street, Honley, Holmfirth, West Yorkshire, HD9 6AH

wiredcoffeeandcake.co.uk | 07598 931448

f wiredcoffeeandcake *☉ wiredcoffeeandcake*

Crunchy rocky road, chewy flapjack, gooey brownies and zingy ginger and lime cake are just a few of the countertop delights to be discovered at this Honley emporium of coffee and cake.

Wired's team of flavoursmiths pair their delicious homemade bakes with Resilience, a bespoke coffee created in collaboration with local roastery Dark Woods. The house blend bursts with juicy-fruit flavours when served black yet hits new vibrantly sweet notes when paired with steamed milk. Those looking to freestyle their coffee and cake match can find even more flavours in regular guest roasts from UK speciality roasteries (available in a range of pourover styles).

TIP ARRIVE EARLY ON THE WEEKEND TO BAG A TABLE AND A BACON BUTTY

Fans of the house beans can take a consignment home via Wired's new reusable tins and even get a discount on future refills. There's also a superb selection of scrumptious peanut butters, jams, sauces and preserves for sale, all sourced from local suppliers.

Established
2018

Key roaster
Dark Woods Coffee

Brewing method
Espresso, V60, Clever Dripper, AeroPress

Machine
Iberital Expression Pro

Grinder
Mahlkonig K30, Anfim Pratica

Opening hours
Fri-Sat
9.30am-3pm
Sun
10am-3pm

REUSABLES ACCEPTED

WIFI

BIKE FRIENDLY

DOGS WELCOME

BUY BEANS IN STORE

OUTDOOR SEATING

HOLMFIRTH

125

75 HOLME COFFEE HOUSE

108 School Street, Holmfirth, West Yorkshire, HD9 7EQ

holmecoffeehouse.co.uk | 01484 684942

f *Holme Coffee House, Holmfirth* ⓘ *holmecoffeehouse*

Brunch isn't confined to the weekend at this lively coffee house in the heart of Holmfirth – in fact, it's not even reserved for the morning as the bill of bougie breakfast-inspired dishes is served all day.

A lengthy list of add-ons enables visitors to customise their order: golden slices of fried halloumi to smashed avo on toast, additional poached eggs to wild mushrooms on sourdough, a side of crisp streaky bacon to a stack of fluffy American pancakes. Those celebrating (or not) will find a glass or two of chilled fizz the perfect brunch mate.

TIP TRY THE HOUSE-FAVE FRENCH TOAST WITH ITS SEASONALLY CHANGING TOPPINGS

Coffee is another all-day speciality at Holme and the house blend, Derek, is sourced from Bean Brothers in Huddersfield. Derek is joined by a monthly guest option from the likes of Hasbean, Kick Back and Girls Who Grind, available as V60.

Such is the popularity of this welcoming space that on weekends there's often a queue for a seat. Don't be deterred, however, as the friendly team are quick to turn the tables and the wait is always worth it.

Established
2019

Key roaster
Bean Brothers
Coffee Company

Brewing method
Espresso, V60

Machine
La Marzocco
Linea Classic

Grinder
Mahlkonig K30 Air

Opening hours
Mon–Thu
9.30am–4pm
Fri–Sat
9.30am–5pm
Sun
10am–4pm

REUSABLES ACCEPTED   WIFI   DOGS WELCOME   BUY BEANS IN STORE

76 BLOC

19a Huddersfield Road, Holmfirth, West Yorkshire, HD9 2JR

bearbeans.co.uk | 07563 244039

bloc_holmfirth

This gorgeous glass-encased building in the heart of Holmfirth has been a speciality hub since 2016. The popular coffee spot was sold in 2022 but, much to the delight of locals, landed in the safe paws of Bear. The Coffee Roasters founder Chris Gregory.

Chris undertook an extensive refurbishment of the space, adding his own touches and redesigning the kitchen in order to refine the food offering. Under its previous ownership it was a local institution for weekend brunching and Chris continued its legacy in this new guise, creating a core range of six dishes which include the likes of brioche french toast with seasonal toppings.

TIP DON'T MISS THE WOOD-FIRED PIZZA EVENINGS IN SUMMER

The coffee offering has seen the biggest overhaul, with house-roasted Bear beans now filling the hoppers. Pourover options have also been added to the bill and, in summer, visitors can enjoy an iced V60 or homemade cold brew on the heated decking.

Love what you're drinking? Get the beans delivered to your door via the Bear Cubscription.

Established
2022

Key roaster
Bear. The Coffee Roasters

Brewing method
Espresso, V60, pourover

Machine
La Marzocco Linea

Grinder
Mahlkonig K30, Anfim Pratica, Eureka Mignon Specialita

Opening hours
Mon–Sun
8am–3pm

REUSABLES ACCEPTED

WIFI

BIKE FRIENDLY

DOGS WELCOME

BUY BEANS IN STORE

COFFEE COURSES

OUTDOOR SEATING

77 BEAR. ROASTERY OUTLET

5a Hollowgate, Holmfirth, West Yorkshire, HD9 2DG

bearbeans.co.uk | 07497 616737

bearbeans_

If you're the kind of person who loves to quiz baristas on flavour profiles, sample bonkers blends and experiment with opinion-splitting single origins then you're overdue a visit to this tiny coffee bar.

With just two seats, this roastery outlet is mostly a take-out situation, but visit during a quiet period and it's the perfect place to slurp exciting coffees and pick the brains of experienced baristas. There are usually around seven coffees to choose from – all fresh from the Bear roastery at The Old Silk Mill – which can be prepared as espresso, V60, AeroPress or cold brew.

TIP NO SPACE TO SIT IN? HEAD TO THE SISTER COFFEE HOUSE AND EATERY ON HUDDERSFIELD ROAD

The line-up rotates regularly but there are a few core roasts such as cold-brew blend Polar Bear (a deliciously smooth chocolate and soft-fruit mash-up for thirst-quenching summer refreshment) and Fozzie (a barmy blend of three naturals which *'opens flavour up wider than the Zambezi'*).

Visitors almost always leave with a bag of coffee to brew at home and those who really fall for Bear's beans sign up for a Cubscription, which gives subscribers the choice of four coffee portfolios each month (including a Wild Bear chosen by the team).

Established
2019

Key roaster
Bear. The Coffee Roasters

Brewing method
Espresso, V60, AeroPress, cold brew

Machine
La Marzocco Linea

Grinder
Mahlkonig K30, Anfim Pratica, Mahlkonig EK43, Eureka Mignon Specialita

Opening hours
Wed-Sat
9am-4pm
Sun
10am-3pm

REUSABLES ACCEPTED | WIFI | BIKE FRIENDLY | DOGS WELCOME | BUY BEANS IN STORE | COFFEE COURSES

78 ON TRACK COFFEE

Mulberry Way, Wakefield, West Yorkshire, WF1 2QN

ontrackcoffee.bigcartel.com | 07943 724816

f On Track Coffee ◎ ontrackcoffee

For most coffee connoisseurs the train station isn't the first stop for a refined cup of coffee, yet for flat white fans in Wakefield it's one of the few places you'll find an excellent brew.

Since opening in September 2022, On Track Coffee has kept commuters and locals expertly caffeinated from its spot within Wakefield Westgate station. Founder Harrison Byrne enlisted Hard Lines in Cardiff to supply the house beans (a rich natural Brazilian) and there are regular guest espresso and filter appearances from Kiss the Hippo, Elsewhere, Assembly and more.

TIP LOOSE CHANGE? ADD IT TO THE TIP JAR AND BAG AN ON TRACK STICKER

Grab a pastry (the almond croissants are particularly special) or treat yourself to one of Mandy's sandwiches, such as the first-class grilled cheese. The drinks menu also offers seasonal specials such as Nutella hot chocolate for the festive period and fresh fruit smoothies, iced coffee and cold brew in the warmer months.

Grabbing a pre-train flattie? Arrive early and give yourself time to sit in and sip from the beautiful ceramic cups. Coffee this good deserves to be savoured.

Established
2022

Key roaster
Hard Lines

Brewing method
Espresso, filter, cold brew

Machine
La Marzocco Linea PB

Grinder
Mahlkonig X54 × 2

Opening hours
Mon, Fri
6.45am–3pm
Tue–Thu
6am–3pm
Sat
8am–3pm

REUSABLES
ACCEPTED

WIFI

BIKE
FRIENDLY

DOGS
WELCOME

BUY BEANS
IN STORE

COFFEE
COURSES

OUTDOOR
SEATING

79 KRA:FT WAKEFIELD

12 Wood Street, Wakefield, West Yorkshire, WF1 2ED

kraftwakefield.co.uk | 07921 180287

f kraftwakefield *ⓞ kraftwakefield*

A visit to this uber-slick coffee shop and cocktail bar in Wakefield is an instant mood booster. The industrial-chic interiors (combining textures of leather, wood and copper) create an upmarket ambience by day and casual intimacy by night.

Originally a barber shop with espresso bar, KRA:FT has evolved since it launched in 2020 and is now a full-blown sister venue to the ever-busy male-grooming salon next door.

TIP COCKTAIL CONNOISSEUR? THE CREATIVE DRINKS MENU GOES WAY BEYOND ESPRESSO MARTINIS

North Star in Leeds keeps the grinder topped up with a steady supply of speciality coffee, while an ever-changing raft of guest blends and single origins make an appearance care of the North's finest indie roasters. If you're after a stellar cup of tea, you'll be spoilt for choice by the selection on offer from Sheffield's Birdhouse Tea Company.

Whether you go boozy or stick to caffeinated thrills, pair your poison with a slice of gooey salted caramel brownie or flaky almond croissant.

Established
2020

Key roaster
North Star
Coffee Roasters

Brewing method
Espresso, V60

Machine
Modbar

Grinder
Mahlkonig EK43,
Mahlkonig E65

Opening hours
Tue–Thu
8am–3pm
Fri–Sat
8am–late
Sun
10am–3pm

REUSABLES ACCEPTED | WIFI | BIKE FRIENDLY | DOGS WELCOME | BUY BEANS IN STORE | COFFEE COURSES | OUTDOOR SEATING

80 THE HEPWORTH WAKEFIELD CAFE

Gallery Walk, Wakefield, West Yorkshire, WF1 5AW

hepworthwakefield.org | 01924 247360

f *thehepworthwakefield* ⊙ *hepworthwakefield*

Chew over the latest exhibition as you chow down on brunch at this contemporary cafe within The Hepworth Wakefield (named after Barbara Hepworth, the celebrated 20th-century artist and sculptor who was brought up in Wakefield).

Since 2021, the cafe has been managed by Carl Fleisher who is committed to improving its eco initiatives. One of his major wins so far has been the conversion of the cafe's food waste into bioenergy to make fuel and fertiliser, which is facilitated by ReFood in Doncaster. *'In a period of just five weeks, 105 kWh of energy was produced through our waste alone,'* explains Carl. *'It's then fed back to the National Grid.'*

TIP SEE THE WEBSITE FOR INFO ON UPCOMING SUPPER CLUBS AND SEASONAL CELEBRATIONS

Sustainability extends to sourcing, and many of the ingredients on the breakfast and lunch menus are grown by local producers. Yorkshire's famous forced rhubarb, for example, is grown just three miles from the gallery and, in season, is used in specials such as cider-braised pork belly with goat's curd and rhubarb.

On the coffee front, a roll call of Northern roasteries provides single-origin guests for batch brew, while London's Square Mile stumps up its ever-reliable Red Brick blend for espresso.

Established
2021

Key roaster
Square Mile
Coffee Roasters

Brewing method
Espresso,
batch brew

Machine
La Marzocco
Linea

Grinder
Mahlkonig EK43,
Mahlkonig E65S
GbW × 2

Opening hours
Tue–Sun
10am–5pm

REUSABLES
ACCEPTED

WIFI

BIKE
FRIENDLY

BUY BEANS
IN STORE

COFFEE
COURSES

81 OLD GEORGE COFFEE HOUSE

14 Market Hill, Barnsley, South Yorkshire, S70 2QE

old-george.co.uk | 01226 695700

f oldgeorgebarn *oldgeorgebarnsley*

Customers rave about the attentive front-of-house team and banging brunches at this quirky cafe in Barnsley. With such a loyal local following, it pays to arrive early on weekends if you want to bag a table.

Hailing from Foundation Coffee Roasters in St Ives, the house blend is a dark-roasted Peruvian and Colombian combo which packs a punch with flavours of chocolate and treacle. The single-origin option, Q'antxabina from Guatemala, is a fruitier affair with notes of green apple, plum, chocolate and hazelnut.

TIP IN A HURRY? GRAB A SLAB OF HOMEMADE BROWNIE WITH YOUR COFFEE TO GO

Brunchtime visitors can enjoy sweet thrills such as pancakes stacked with Biscoff and strawberries, alongside the full gamut of traditional brekkie items (got to keep the purists happy) such as eggs benny and breakfast sandwiches stuffed with fried eggs and sausages.

Furry friends are very welcome and get their own menu, which includes puppuccinos and doggy sausages.

Established
2017

Key roaster
Foundation
Coffee Roasters

Brewing method
Espresso, V60,
AeroPress

Machine
Faema E71

Grinder
Faema
Groundbreaker

Opening hours
Mon–Sun
9am–4pm

BARNSLEY

REUSABLES ACCEPTED   WIFI   DOGS WELCOME   BUY BEANS IN STORE   OUTDOOR SEATING

132

82 EVE KITCHEN

380 Sharrow Vale Road, Sheffield, South Yorkshire, S11 8ZP

07738 280638

◎ eve.kitchen

If your favourite side to a silky flat white is a pillowy doughnut, you'll be champing at the bit to visit this speciality cafe-bakery in Sheffield.

The Eve Kitchen bakers incorporate local and seasonal ingredients in their perfected 48-hour process, which results in a selection of pulse-racingly good artisan doughnuts. Unctuous fillings are switched up weekly and include irresistible combos such as Yorkshire rhubarb puree with lemon curd cream, indulgent chocolate and pistachio crumb, and Med-style saffron and blood orange.

TIP CAN'T DECIDE WHICH DOUGH TO PICK? THE ESPRESSO YUM YUMS ARE UNREAL

The designer dough is the perfect companion to London-roasted Assembly coffee, which the Eve baristas craft into crema-rich espresso and fruit-forward batch brew. In summer, espresso is partnered with homemade soft-serve ice cream (flavours change weekly) for next-level affogatos.

Don't leave without popping next door to the cafe's lifestyle shop to browse ceramic V60s and coffee cups, books, artisan chocolate and homemade jams and curds.

Established
2015

Key roaster
Assembly Coffee

Brewing method
Espresso, filter

Machine
Londinium II

Grinder
Mythos

Opening hours
Tue–Sun
10.30am–4pm

REUSABLES ACCEPTED WIFI BIKE FRIENDLY DOGS WELCOME BUY BEANS IN STORE OUTDOOR SEATING

YORKSHIRE
ROASTERIES

83 THREE RIDINGS COFFEE

Unit 1e Bessingby Way, Bridlington, East Yorkshire, YO16 4SJ

threeridingscoffee.co.uk | 01262 425098

f *threeridingscoffee* ⊙ *threeridingscoffee*

The team at this Bridlington indie are so proud of their region that they named their roastery after the Three Ridings of Yorkshire (an ancient subdivision of the east, west and north of the county, before it was recategorised in the 1970s) and created a logo to reflect the geographical shape of the original Ridings.

It's a fitting brand for a roastery that celebrates its heritage and aims to put East Yorkshire on the map as a destination for quality coffee. The team also want to break down some of the snobbery associated with the industry. Their stance that *'we all start somewhere'* is core to the their educational focus: *'Going from a mug of Kenco to a fruity micro-lot AeroPress is a process – we're not here to judge,'* say founders Leo Jarvis and Jordan Cavalli.

'PUTTING EAST YORKSHIRE ON THE MAP AS A DESTINATION FOR QUALITY COFFEE'

For an introduction to Three Ridings' coffees, check out the Classic Collection – the bread and butter of the roastery's catalogue. After something unusual? Explore the Limited Coffees range, which focuses on interesting tasting notes and processing methods.

Beans are packaged in reusable glass bottles and include a card crammed with info on each coffee's cherry-to-cup journey. Wholesale orders are also packaged in reusable containers.

Established
2020

Roaster make and size
Besca BSC-15 15kg,
Aillio Bullet R1
V2 1kg

BRIDLINGTON

OPEN BY
INVITE

COFFEE
COURSES

BUY BEANS
ONLINE

BUY BEANS
IN STORE

84 ROOST COFFEE & ROASTERY

6 Talbot Yard, Yorkersgate, Malton, North Yorkshire, YO17 7FT

roostcoffee.co.uk | 01653 697635

f roostcoffeeandroastery *roost_coffee*

The aim of this family-run business is to provide high-quality speciality coffee at an affordable price. It's a focus that's been woven into the fabric of Roost ever since its inception by owners Ruth and David Elkington, who set up the coffee shop and roastery in 2015.

'SIGN UP TO THE ROOST COFFEE CLUB FOR A HANDPICKED SELECTION OF BEANS EACH MONTH'

Today the team supply a wide selection of blends and single origins to customers through both the website and Roost's espresso bar and retail shop in Talbot Yard. Avid coffee fans can also sign up to the Roost Coffee Club to receive a handpicked selection of beans each month, which arrive whole or ground to their specification.

The coffee is sourced through trusted importers and at any one time the collection includes at least three blends, a chemical-free Swiss Water decaf and 12 single origins from across the globe.

Buying for a fellow coffee lover? The Letterbox Coffee Selection is a great gift and includes five single origins beautifully wrapped in 100 per cent recyclable packaging.

Established
2015

Roaster make and size
Joper BSR 15
KIT 15kg,
Diedrich IR-12 12kg

CAFE ON SITE

OPEN BY INVITE

BUY BEANS ONLINE

85 CASA ESPRESSO COFFEE ROASTERS

Unit 1 Briar Rhydding House, Briar Rhydding, Otley Road, Shipley, West Yorkshire, BD17 7JW

casaespresso.co.uk | 01274 595841

f casaespresso ⓞ *casa_espresso*

The Di Rienzo family have influenced Bradford's food and drink scene for almost 50 years: they opened the city's first Italian pizzeria in 1974, turned their attention to speciality coffee in 2000 and son Nino opened Bradford's first independent roastery in 2014.

Working alongside Nino at Casa is head roaster and barista-trainer Jonnie, account manager Jacob and dispatch manager David. In the past year the roastery has scaled up, moving to bigger premises and welcoming a new 15kg Joper roaster to enable increased production. Before firing it up, each lot is tested to explore different roast profiles in the search for the sweet spot that enhances the beans' unique aromatics and flavours.

'THE PACKAGING OF EVERY RETAIL BAG OF CASA BEANS IS NOW FULLY RECYCLABLE'

The coffee is sourced from independent green-bean importers who share the team's ethical values of supporting farmers, workers and their local communities. As well as partnering with World Coffee Research to support the future of the industry, the team have prioritised sustainability and the packaging of every retail bag of Casa beans is now fully recyclable.

Local coffee fans can sharpen their skills at one of the new Home Barista classes, which cover everything they need to know to craft the perfect flat white.

Established
2014

Roaster make and size
Joper BSR 15 KIT 15kg,
Probat
Probatone 5 5kg

OPEN TO THE PUBLIC

COFFEE COURSES

BUY BEANS ONLINE

BUY BEANS IN STORE

86 WHITE ROSE COFFEE ROASTERS

6-8 Hall Street, Halifax, West Yorkshire, HX1 5AY
whiterosecoffeeroasters.co.uk | 01422 347734
f *whiteroseroasters* ⊙ *white.rose.coffee.roasters*

There's no shortage of choice for coffee lovers browsing the online shop of this independent Halifax roastery. With over 20 single origins and six bespoke blends (including three Great Taste award winners) available at any time, it's a treasure trove for those who enjoy trying out coffees from different origins.

From Burundi to Colombia, Jamaica to Papua New Guinea, founder Robert Cooper scours the world for beans of quality and provenance. They're bronzed on a duo of Toper roasters by a team with over 30 years of experience in the industry, before being packaged in fully recyclable bags.

'A TREASURE TROVE FOR THOSE WHO ENJOY TRYING OUT COFFEES FROM DIFFERENT ORIGINS'

Those who eschew experimentation in favour of comforting familiarity will find it in White Rose's selection of blends: Cattle Market Espresso and Hikers Inspiration are popular and can be bought as whole bean or pre-ground. Ambitious coffee fans can even buy green beans to roast at home.

Coffee shops and restaurants looking to craft their own bespoke roast can take advantage of White Rose's white label service.

Established
2015

Roaster make and size
Toper 30kg,
Toper 5kg

OPEN BY INVITE **BUY BEANS ONLINE** **BUY BEANS IN STORE**

87 DARK WOODS COFFEE

Holme Mills, West Slaithwaite Road, Marsden, Huddersfield, West Yorkshire, HD7 6LS

darkwoodscoffee.co.uk | 01484 843141

f *darkwoodscoffee* ◎ *darkwoodscoffee*

This roastery, barista school and pop-up cafe may be housed in a Victorian textile mill, its beans roasted on a vintage Probat and the building encircled by ancient woodland, but Dark Woods is far from old-school thanks to its adventurous ethos and contemporary methods.

An exciting blend of tradition and innovation has won the roastery multiple awards, including over 70 Great Taste awards (and two of its Golden Forks). This success is no surprise when you know that its trio of directors (Damian Blackburn, Paul Meikle-Janney and Ian Agnew) have between them judged the Cup of Excellence, helped organise the World Coffee Championships, co-written the SCA barista qualifications and chaired Farmers' Voice Radio (a charity that uses local radio stations to assist coffee farmers around the world).

'DARK WOODS HAS WON MULTIPLE AWARDS, INCLUDING OVER 70 GREAT TASTE AWARDS'

A particular benefit of the team's experience and expertise is the web of producers and distributors keen to share their best beans with them, knowing their greens will be in good hands. This has led to Dark Woods' Producer Series, which showcases exclusive seasonal micro-lots and runs alongside its Core Range of winning blends and single origins.

Established
2013

Roaster make and size
Probat G45 45kg,
Probat UG22 22kg,
Probat 5 5kg

HUDDERSFIELD

OPEN BY INVITE

COFFEE COURSES

BUY BEANS ONLINE

BUY BEANS IN STORE

88 BEAR. THE COFFEE ROASTERS

The Old Silk Mill, Moll Springs Mills, Honley, West Yorkshire, HD4 7DN

bearbeans.co.uk | 07497 616737

bearbeans_

Before the pandemic turned the world upside down, Chris Gregory was a musician. The lockdowns brought his funk and soul gigs and TV-music composition work to a screeching halt and so, ever the creative, Chris turned his attention to something entirely different: speciality coffee.

A chance encounter with a naturally processed El Porvenir Nicaraguan coffee that tasted of kiwi and strawberry shifted the course of Chris' life, resulting in him investing in a 500g roaster. Three years on, Chris is completely immersed in the speciality world and has carved out a coffee brand that focuses on sourcing exceptional beans from farms of note.

The roastery recently relocated to a newly refurbished space in a converted mill in Honley to make room for cupping sessions, barista courses and a gleaming new custom roaster. It's joined by a Bear coffee shop in Holmfirth, where locals and tourists head to pick up excellent takeaway coffee and beans to brew at home, and Bloc, a sister coffee house and eatery (also in Holmfirth), which became part of the Bear family in 2022.

Established
2019

Roaster make and size
Custom roaster 4.8kg

'A COFFEE BRAND THAT FOCUSES ON SOURCING EXCEPTIONAL BEANS FROM FARMS OF NOTE'

'What I enjoy most is creating exceptional experiences for my customers,' explains Chris. *'Whether it's someone who doesn't know much about speciality popping into the shop or a long-term customer ordering online, my goal is to give them the best coffee experience possible.'*

CAFE ON SITE

BUY BEANS ONLINE

BUY BEANS IN STORE

CREATE A SLICE OF CAFE CULTURE AT HOME

Indy Cafe Cookbook Volume 2 features 40 recipes from the UK's hero cafes and roasteries.

Turn weekend mornings into something special.

89 GRUMPY MULE

Bewley's, Bent Ley Road, Meltham, Holmfirth, West Yorkshire, HD9 4EP

grumpymule.co.uk | 01494 412408

f *grumpymulecoffee* ⊙ *grumpy_mule*

Founded in 2006, Grumpy Mule aims to make customers smile with its irreverent, tongue-in-cheek brand.

While fun is a focus, the roastery, which is nestled in the Holme Valley, seemingly never sleeps. Two huge gas-fired Probat roasters and a 35kg Loring Smart turn out a staggering volume of top-grade coffee each week, which is delivered to Grumpy Mule's hospitality, retail and direct customers in Yorkshire and beyond.

It's racked up a whopping 40 Great Taste awards since 2014 – including a three-star award for its Landscape Espresso blend in 2022 – so these roasters clearly know a thing or two about crafting a winning cup of coffee. Those who want to glean some roasting wisdom or perfect their barista skills should sign up to one of Grumpy Mule's SCA-accredited courses.

'A WHOPPING 40 GREAT TASTE AWARDS SINCE 2014'

A company-wide belief that quality drives sustainability sees a focus on Fairtrade, direct trade and relationships with organic farmers and growers. The result is that everyone benefits from Grumpy Mule's participation in the coffee cycle.

Established
2006

Roaster make and size
Probat G120 120kg,
Probat G60 60kg,
Loring Kestrel 35kg

COFFEE COURSES

BUY BEANS ONLINE

90 DANELAW COFFEE

Unit D11 Meltham Mills Industrial Estate, Holmfirth, Yorkshire, HD9 4DS

danelaw.coffee | 07506 900331

f danelawcoffee *@ danelawcoffee*

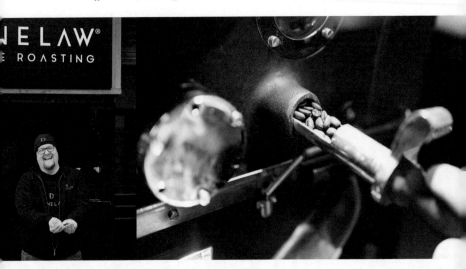

F ounded in April 2022 by two-time Coffee in Good Spirits champion David Jameson, this up and coming roastery takes its moniker from the Viking name for the north and east of England. Located in a former tractor factory, it's cultivating a reputation as another high-quality Yorkshire coffee roastery.

David has 17 years of experience in the coffee industry – from high-street chains to small-scale roasteries – and is using it to help make speciality coffee accessible to all. Minimalist packaging (nominated for an SCA Coffee Design Award) carries concise information about the coffee within. Visit the online shop and you'll encounter clear language and relatable flavour references.

Established
2022

Roaster make and size
Giesen W6E 6kg,
Aillio Bullet 1kg

'MINIMALIST PACKAGING CARRIES CONCISE INFORMATION ABOUT THE COFFEE WITHIN'

Danelaw's catalogue of beans provides a mix of blends and single origins. Several have won Great Taste awards, including the lightly roasted Fjødr and the Mjölnir – a darker blend that includes naturally processed robusta.

Planning a trip to Holmfirth? Book in for a roastery visit and, if you time it right, David might rustle up one of the best Irish coffees you've ever tasted.

HOLMFIRTH

OPEN BY INVITE

BUY BEANS ONLINE

91 FORGE COFFEE ROASTERS

Don Road, Sheffield, South Yorkshire, S9 2TF
forgecoffeeroasters.co.uk | 01142 441361
f forgeroasters *⊙ forgeroasters*

Nods to Sheffield's industrial history run through Forge Coffee Roasters – from the team's baker-boy caps and meticulously trimmed moustaches to their vintage delivery truck and workshop laden with forging memorabilia.

While the roastery takes its aesthetic inspiration from the city's steelmaking heritage, the creation of its coffee is firmly rooted in contemporary innovation. A sleek Giesen W30 is the roastery's workhorse and churns out small batches of exquisite speciality-grade coffee.

'BRIMMING WITH NOTES OF BLACK CHERRY, DARK CHOCOLATE, TOFFEE AND VANILLA'

Forge's core collection comprises four blends, one of which is a decaf. The consistent crowd-pleaser is Invicta, a delicious espresso brimming with notes of black cherry, dark chocolate, toffee and vanilla.

The team also experiment with single-origin coffees processed in unusual ways: the latest is their first anaerobic micro-lot from Johan Vergara at the Las Flores farm in Colombia.

Established
2015

Roaster make and size
Giesen W30 30kg,
Giesen W1A 1kg,
IKAWA

OPEN BY INVITE

BUY BEANS ONLINE

'O
BUY BEANS IN STORE

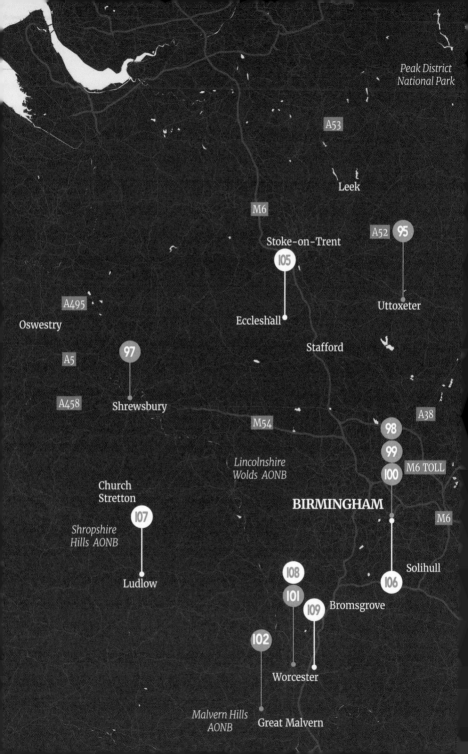

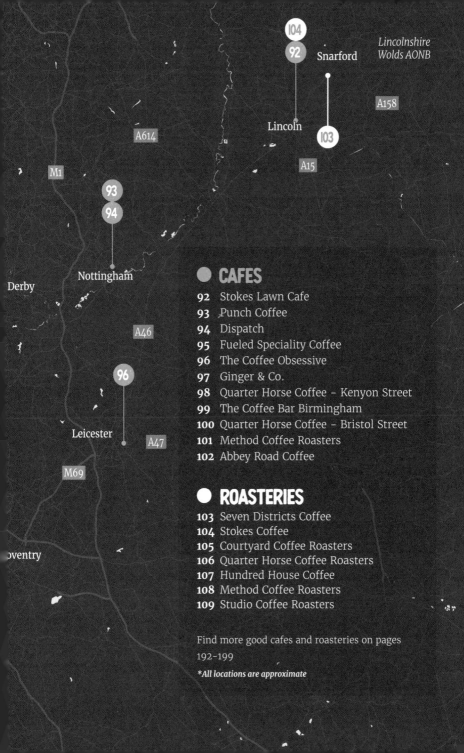

104
92
Snarford

Lincolnshire Wolds AONB

A158

A614

Lincoln

103

M1

A15

93
94

Nottingham

Derby

A46

96

A47

Leicester

M69

oventry

CAFES

92 Stokes Lawn Cafe
93 Punch Coffee
94 Dispatch
95 Fueled Speciality Coffee
96 The Coffee Obsessive
97 Ginger & Co.
98 Quarter Horse Coffee – Kenyon Street
99 The Coffee Bar Birmingham
100 Quarter Horse Coffee – Bristol Street
101 Method Coffee Roasters
102 Abbey Road Coffee

ROASTERIES

103 Seven Districts Coffee
104 Stokes Coffee
105 Courtyard Coffee Roasters
106 Quarter Horse Coffee Roasters
107 Hundred House Coffee
108 Method Coffee Roasters
109 Studio Coffee Roasters

Find more good cafes and roasteries on pages 192–199

All locations are approximate

92 STOKES LAWN CAFE

Suite 1, The Lawn, Union Road, Lincoln, Lincolnshire, LN1 3BU

stokescoffee.com | 01522 581921

f *stokescoffee* ⊙ *stokescoffee*

There aren't many indie cafes that can boast a 121-year history, so Stokes in Lincoln is somewhat unusual. Run by the fourth generation of the Stokes family, the business comprises a roastery and four coffee shops.

The company HQ and roastery is housed in the former Lincoln Asylum, an impressive 200-year-old building a short walk from Lincoln Castle. It's also home to Stokes Lawn Cafe which, despite its historic setting, is furnished in a contemporary industrial style with upcycled furniture and reclaimed scaffolding. Its most surprising feature, however, is Lulu: a life-size orca whale made from old car bumpers and coffee machine parts suspended from the ceiling.

TIP HEAD TO THE VIEWING GALLERY TO WATCH THE STOKES ROASTERY IN ACTION WHILE YOU SIP

Take a pew below the colossal art installation to browse the extensive coffee line-up. Most regulars opt for a cup of the ever-popular filter, which was first created by Stokes more than 50 years ago to emulate the smooth rich taste of Jamaican Blue Mountain.

Be sure to check out the new weekend evening dining experience, Late at the Lawn, where you can feast on a selection of small plates, sip cocktails and immerse yourself in the classy vibe.

Established
1902

Key roaster
Stokes Coffee

Brewing method
Espresso, V60, batch brew, AeroPress, cold brew, cafetiere

Machine
Sanremo Opera

Grinder
Fiorenzato F64

Opening hours
Mon–Sat
8.30am–4pm
Sun
9am–4pm

REUSABLES ACCEPTED | WIFI | BIKE FRIENDLY | DOGS WELCOME | BUY BEANS IN STORE | COFFEE COURSES | OUTDOOR SEATING

LINCOLN

150

93 PUNCH COFFEE

215 Mansfield Road, Nottingham, NG1 3FS

punch.coffee

f punchcoffeenotts *⌾ punchcoffeenottingham*

This new coffee shop on Nottingham's Mansfield Road is a collaborative project between two families: property and design pros Ben and Kellie Bradley and vicar and events caterer Amy and Adam Jones.

The couples have combined their expertise to create a coffee shop that not only serves delicious speciality coffee and homemade food but also provides a warm and friendly hub for the local community. The result is a welcoming spot where people meet to connect and unwind.

TIP PAIR YOUR COFFEE WITH A GLUTEN-FREE BROWNIE OR THE HOUSE FAVE BLUEBERRY MUFFIN

Chef Adam oversees the food menus, which have proved so popular since opening in September 2022 that they've already grown to meet customer demand. Everything from the signature bakes to the toasties and breakfast dishes are made from scratch in the Punch kitchen each morning.

Equal care and attention goes into the coffee, which uses single-origin beans from local roastery Outpost. Espresso is the house serve, but if you prefer filter there are batch brew options available too.

Established
2022

Key roaster
Outpost Coffee
Roasters

Brewing method
Espresso,
batch brew

Machine
La Marzocco
Linea Classic

Grinder
Mazzer Super Jolly

Opening hours
Mon–Sun
8am–4pm

REUSABLES
ACCEPTED

WIFI

BIKE
FRIENDLY

DOGS
WELCOME

BUY BEANS
IN STORE

OUTDOOR
SEATING

94 DISPATCH

2 Goosegate, Nottingham, NG1 1FF

dispatchcoffees.co.uk | 07862 646486

@ dispatchcoffees

Just five minutes spent inside this kaleidoscopic coffee shop is guaranteed to raise the spirits. Barbie-pink walls with jade green panelling, a sunshine yellow La Marzocco coffee machine and a terrazzo-print brew bar add to the joyful atmosphere created by Dispatch's friendly baristas.

The bright decor, cafe name and motto ('pas de souci', translating to 'no worries') were inspired by Wes Anderson film *The French Dispatch*.

TIP CAN'T DECIDE WHICH SWEET TREAT TO PICK? LOOK NO FURTHER THAN THE WARM BANANA BREAD

Take time to soak up the kooky surroundings: order a cafetiere and slice of homemade vegan Biscoff cake, settle into one of the plush velvet chairs and let the caffeine buzz and eclectic styling transport you to a realm of Anderson-esque fantasy.

The coffee in your cup will likely be a single-origin Mexican roasted by Outpost in Nottingham, but the bean offering is occasionally shaken up to feature guest roasts from the likes of Hard Lines in Cardiff.

Lunchtime visitors should add a toastie to their order. The Dispatch crew specialise in grilled goods and craft a noteworthy pastrami number that oozes with Swiss cheese, sauerkraut and mustard mayo. Plant-based? The vegan version is a dynamite alternative.

Established
2022

Key roaster
Outpost Coffee

Brewing method
Espresso, cafetiere

Machine
La Marzocco

Grinder
Mazzer Luigi

Opening hours
Mon–Fri
8.30am–7pm
Sat
10am–7pm
Sun
10am–4pm

WIFI DOGS WELCOME OUTDOOR SEATING

95 FUELED SPECIALITY COFFEE

4 Carters Square, Uttoxeter, Staffordshire, ST14 7FN

fueledcoffee.co.uk

f *fueledcoffeeuk* ⊚ *fueledcoffeeuk*

In 2017, Matt and Joe retired from professional dancing with a dream to make their next adventure the launch of their own coffee shop. To learn the tricks of the trade, Joe enrolled at the London School of Coffee and, in 2021, the couple opened Fueled in the heart of Uttoxeter.

The bright and spacious cafe brings a cosmopolitan vibe to the market town and is known for its fun-loving staff, belt-busting brunches and quality coffee.

Buxton Coffee Roasters supplies the goods for the house blend, a fusion of Brazilian, Ethiopian and Thai beans with notes of chocolate, hazelnut and citrusy zing. If you're after something more complex, there's also a rotating selection of guest single-origins to try.

TIP DOWNLOAD THE DIGITAL LOYALTY CARD TO CLAIM A FREE HOT DRINK

Leading the food line-up is The Auckland (a bagel topped with pesto, avocado, streaky bacon, cream cheese and balsamic glaze), a customer fave inspired by Matt and Joe's travels in New Zealand. Fans of a trad full English love The Fully Fueled for its hash-brown nuggets and crisp black pudding.

Drawing on their roots in the entertainment industry, Matt and Joe also host regular events including comedy evenings, creative workshops and mediumship nights.

Established
2021

Key roaster
Buxton Coffee Roasters

Brewing method
Espresso, V60, Chemex, Curtis Seraphim

Machine
Sanremo Opera

Grinder
Mahlkonig E65S, Mahlkonig E65S GbW, Mahlkonig EK43, Mahlkonig E80

Opening hours
Mon–Thu
7.30am–5pm
Fri–Sat
7.30am–6pm
Sun
9am–4pm

WIFI BIKE FRIENDLY DOGS WELCOME BUY BEANS IN STORE OUTDOOR SEATING

UTTOXETER

153

96 THE COFFEE OBSESSIVE

53 Francis Street, Leicester, LE2 2BE

thecoffeeobsessive.com | 07950 355201

@ *thecoffeeobsessive*

In 2009, Iqbal Mahomed moved into an apartment opposite Melbourne coffee institution Proud Mary. Interest piqued, he immersed himself in Australian cafe culture and, in 2015, returned to London with an itch that needed scratching.

Three years later, Iqbal left his career in fashion to search for the best coffee on the planet under a new alias: The Coffee Obsessive. Post adventures, he returned to his home-city of Leicester with the aim of recreating his global coffee experiences in his own dream cafe, which he opened in December 2020.

TIP TOUR THE WORLD'S BEST ROASTERIES VIA THE GUEST ESPRESSO SLOT

Iqbal's design expertise shines through in the beautiful interior and finishings. A stripped-back ode to contemporary minimalism, the styling is only rivalled by the quality of coffee on offer.

The house espresso comes from Leeds' North Star and the guest hopper is refreshed regularly with beans from Dak, Sweven and other European faves. It's a similar story on the retail shelves, which are packed with coffees from Onyx, Bonanza, Five Elephant and Gardelli, to name a few.

Established
2020

Key roaster
Multiple roasteries

Brewing method
Espresso, V60,
Kalita Wave,
batch brew

Machine
La Marzocco
Linea PB X

Grinder
Anfim SP II,
Mahlkonig
E65S GbW,
Mahlkonig EK43

Opening hours
Mon-Fri
8am–4pm
Sat–Sun
9am–4pm

LEICESTER

 REUSABLES ACCEPTED

 WIFI

 DOGS WELCOME

 BUY BEANS IN STORE

154

97 GINGER & CO.

30-31 Princess Street, Shrewsbury, Shropshire, SY1 1LW

gingerandcocoffee.com | 07830 704090

f gingerandcocoffee *ⓞ ginger_and_co_coffee*

It's natural to low-key freak out when your fave local cafe changes hands, but Ginger & Co. regulars didn't need to worry when Melody, Martina and Caterina took over in April 2022 as the trio were veteran baristas of the Shropshire hangout.

They continued the existing partnership with Method Coffee Roasters so the espresso offering, a bespoke blend from the Worcester outfit, is as delicious as ever. It's joined by single-origin guest options from some of the UK's top roasteries.

TIP PLANS FOR COFFEE-TASTING EVENINGS ARE IN THE PIPELINE

While the baristas prep your pick of the coffee list, find a table in the cosy space and peruse the menu of seasonal brunch and lunch dishes. Local produce is put to work in a line-up that includes an impressive assortment of veggie, vegan and gluten-free options.

The homemade kimchi, cheddar and mayo toastie is a plant-based crowd-pleaser, as is the coeliac-friendly Nourishing Bowl of homemade hummus, grains, spiced carrots, chilli edamame beans, red-cabbage slaw, tahini, toasted seeds and nuts. Mains are best chased with something sweet from the sprawling supply of homebaked goodies on the counter.

Established
2015

Key roaster
Method Coffee Roasters

Brewing method
Espresso, V60, pourover

Machine
La Marzocco Linea AV

Grinder
Mahlkonig K30, Mahlkonig EK43

Opening hours
Mon–Thu
8.30am–3pm
Sat
8.30am–4pm
Sun
10am–3pm

REUSABLES ACCEPTED   WIFI   BIKE FRIENDLY   DOGS WELCOME   BUY BEANS IN STORE

98 QUARTER HORSE COFFEE - KENYON STREET

10 Kenyon Street, Birmingham, B18 6AR

quarterhorsecoffee.com | 01212 745740

f quarterhorsecoffee © *quarterhorsecoffee*

Unveiled in January 2023, this new cafe may be small in size but it's mighty in significance for Quarter Horse owner Nathan Retzel and team. Housed in their new roasting site in Birmingham's historic Jewellery Quarter, it's a destination for real coffee connoisseurs.

Grab a seat at the bar and soak up the surroundings. Resting on the peach and cream countertop is a slick new La Marzocco KB90 in a mirrored finish, just one of the elements that contributes to the tactile engaging environment designed to heighten the sensory coffee-drinking experience.

TIP ASK NICELY AND YOU MIGHT GET A TOUR OF THE ROASTING ROOM

Every month the menu showcases a different origin on both espresso and filter. Visit in July to try the Colombian coffee, return in August and you'll be served Costa Rican beans. Usually reserved exclusively for Quarter Horse's subscribers, these coffees can only be bought at the Kenyon Street venue.

Pair the experience with a fresh pastry or cake (crafted by local bakeries) and, before you leave, browse the retail shelves crammed with beans, brewing accessories, reusable cups and a range of manual and electric grinders.

Established
2023

Key roaster
Quarter Horse Coffee

Brewing method
Espresso, filter, Tone Touch 03

Machine
La Marzocco KB90

Grinder
Mahlkonig E65S GbW

Opening hours
Mon-Fri
7.30am-2pm
Sat
9am-4pm

BIRMINGHAM

REUSABLES ACCEPTED

WIFI

DOGS WELCOME

BUY BEANS IN STORE

COFFEE COURSES

OUTDOOR SEATING

156

99 THE COFFEE BAR BIRMINGHAM

10 Temple Row, Birmingham, B2 5HG

thecoffeebarbrum.com | 07903 113820

f thecoffeebarbrum *◎ thecoffeebarbrum*

Neophiles who enjoy sniffing out new and interesting beans can scratch the itch at this contemporary coffee shop and retail space on Birmingham's Temple Row.

A constant stream of coffees from some of Europe's notable roasteries keeps the offering fresh: La Cabra, Manhattan, DAK, Friedhats, Dark Arts, Obadiah and Colonna have all made appearances. The team have recently introduced a frozen dose menu, which enables connoisseurs to sample incredibly rare single-origin beans they won't find in other local coffee shops.

TIP SAVE SPACE FOR SOMETHING SPECIAL FROM A SEASONAL COLLECTION OF BAKES AND PASTRIES

Despite the tempting range, it is Square Mile's Red Brick blend that the team chose as the house espresso thanks to its notes of plum, blackberry, caramel and chocolate. A second espresso, a rotating seasonal single-origin, gives visitors the choice of two contrasting coffees.

Keen home brewers will find everything they need in a retail section that includes kit such as scales, grinders and V60s. Need help? Ask the baristas – they're super knowledgeable and happy to recommend the best buy for your kitchen set-up.

Established
2020

Key roaster
Square Mile
Coffee Roasters

Brewing method
Espresso, pourover

Machine
La Marzocco

Grinder
Mythos One × 2,
Mahlkonig EK43

Opening hours
Mon–Fri
7.30am–5.30pm
Sat
10am–6pm
Sun
10.30am–4.30pm

REUSABLES ACCEPTED | WIFI | BIKE FRIENDLY | DOGS WELCOME | BUY BEANS IN STORE | COFFEE COURSES | OUTDOOR SEATING

Coffee,
Tastings
Talks,
Music,
+ More

BIRMINGHAM COFFEE FESTIVAL

Custard
Factory
Digbeth

8th + 9th
July 2023

@birminghamcoffeefestival
www.birminghamcoffeefestival.com

100 QUARTER HORSE COFFEE - BRISTOL STREET

88-90 Bristol Street, Birmingham, B5 7AH

quarterhorsecoffee.com | 01214 489660

f quarterhorsecoffee *quarterhorsecoffee*

Step into Quarter Horse's original Bristol Street venue and it won't take long to understand why it's a speciality institution in the city. Formerly a hybrid roastery and cafe space (the roasting has moved to a new site in the Jewellery Quarter), this bright and roomy coffee shop is where Birmingham's speciality fans head for their fix.

Order a flat white to experience the house Dark Horse Espresso, a blend of Costa Rican and Brazilian beans delivering notes of brown sugar, orange and dried fruit. Alternatively, explore the regularly rotating filters which are served with an origin card to enlighten the sipper on the provenance of their coffee.

TIP FOR ONE OF BIRMINGHAM'S BEST BREAKFASTS ORDER THE EGGS BENEDICT

An equally thoughtful food menu is updated seasonally and offers a range of vegetarian and vegan options. However, for a simple coffee and carb pairing, look no further than the counter stacked with fresh pastries.

Natural light spills through huge windows to illuminate the high-ceilinged space, making the cafe a favourite with weekday laptop warriors and weekend brunch hunters alike. In summer, head to the suntrap courtyard to sip in the sunshine.

Established
2012

Key roaster
Quarter
Horse Coffee

Brewing method
Espresso,
Kalita Wave

Machine
La Marzocco KB90

Grinder
Mahlkonig EK43 S,
Mythos GBW,
Mahlkonig E65S
GbW

Opening hours
Tue-Fri
8am-4pm
Sat-Sun
9am-3pm

REUSABLES
ACCEPTED

WIFI

BIKE
FRIENDLY

DOGS
WELCOME

BUY BEANS
IN STORE

COFFEE
COURSES

OUTDOOR
SEATING

101 METHOD COFFEE ROASTERS

50-51 Cherry Tree Walk, Worcester, Worcestershire, WR1 3BH

methodroastery.com | 01905 780070

📷 *methodcoffeearches*

Voted one of the best independent coffee shops in the world by *Financial Times* readers, this roastery-cafe in a renovated railway arch enjoys a dedicated following.

Method has a lovely community vibe, which comes as a result of long-standing baristas greeting regulars by name and families gathering round tables to catch up in the inviting space. The ginormous glass frontage floods the room with natural light and creates cosy warmth, even on chilly winter days.

TIP EXTRA-CURRICULAR EVENTS INCLUDE LATTE-ART THROWDOWNS, DJ NIGHTS AND SUMMER BARBECUES

The roastery is located at the back of the cafe, so if you time your visit right you'll be sipping to the rhythmic sound of the Probat roaster chugging away on the next batch. At the bar, there are always at least four types of beans, plus a decaf, on offer from Method's ever-revolving selection. Small-batch micro-lots and seasonal limited-edition roasts feature too, so it's worth asking the team what's on that day.

Homemade cakes, bakes and pastries are on hand to quell rumbling stomachs and calm any caffeine rush from the coffee tasting flight that comprises one coffee prepared three ways.

Established
2018

Key roaster
Method Coffee Roasters

Brewing method
Espresso, V60, cold brew, AeroPress

Machine
La Marzocco Linea PB ABR

Grinder
Mahlkonig EK43

Opening hours
Thu–Sun
10am–4pm

WIFI

DOGS WELCOME

OUTDOOR SEATING

102 ABBEY ROAD COFFEE

11 Abbey Road, Great Malvern, Worcestershire, WR14 3ES
abbeyroadcoffee.co.uk | 07947 209886
f abbeyroadcoffee ☺ *abbeyroadcoffee*

Taking its name from the street on which it resides and owner Tom Floyd's love of The Beatles, Abbey Road Coffee is the perfect space to rejuvenate after a bracing ramble over the Malvern Hills.

The decor is industrial chic in style – bare-bulb lighting, wooden furniture and fittings – while the vibe is relaxed. An illuminated wall sign reminds customers to just 'let it be' as they unwind with flat whites and pastries.

TIP ON BALMY DAYS, NAB A TABLE IN THE LITTLE COURTYARD AREA

The house blend comes courtesy of Method Coffee Roasters in Worcester, which the baristas turn into silky espresso on a La Marzocco Linea. Brews are best married with a bake from the countertop collection. The pièce de résistance is the almond croissant from Peter Cooks Bread in Bishops Frome: a flaky croissant soaked in almond syrup, generously filled with homemade almond cream and coated with flaked almonds and icing sugar.

If you can't get enough of the Abbey Road Coffee experience, a second helping can be had at the new sister site within the Malvern Active gym complex.

Established
2015

Key roaster
Method Coffee Roasters

Brewing method
Espresso, V60

Machine
La Marzocco Linea ABR

Grinder
Mahlkonig E65S × 3

Opening hours
Mon–Sat
8am–5pm
Sun
8am–4pm

REUSABLES ACCEPTED | WIFI | BIKE FRIENDLY | DOGS WELCOME | BUY BEANS IN STORE | COFFEE COURSES | OUTDOOR SEATING

HUNDRED
HOUSE COFFEE

THE
MIDLANDS
ROASTERIES

103 SEVEN DISTRICTS COFFEE

Farmers Arms, Market Rasen Road, Lincoln, Lincolnshire, LN2 3RD

sevendistrictscoffee.com | 01673 885901

f *sevendistrictscoffee* ⊙ *sevendistrictscoffee*

In 2019, Ben Southall and Ellis Purvis blended their passions for speciality coffee, storytelling and their home county of Lincolnshire to create a roastery housed in a former pub.

The founders named the roastery after the county's sub-regions in recognition of the area's importance to their coffee journey. Ben and Ellis explain: '*Lincolnshire is where we sipped our first coffee, burnt our first bean and celebrated our first roast – perfecting our craft as we grew.*'

The duo have spent the past few years honing their talents further, creating an excellent range of eight unique roasts (seven single origins and a blend).

'LINCOLNSHIRE IS WHERE WE SIPPED OUR FIRST COFFEE, BURNT OUR FIRST BEAN AND CELEBRATED OUR FIRST ROAST'

To help coffee fans get the most out of every bag of beans, the story of each roast's cherry-to-cup journey is revealed on the packaging, along with the Lincolnshire fable after which it is named.

Roasting takes place on two custom-made machines (a single roaster couldn't keep up with demand) with the fruits of these labours sold wholesale, and online and in-store for at-home customers. They also feed the hoppers of Seven Districts' sister coffee shops in Nettleham and Langworthgate.

Established
2019

Roaster make and size
Custom built roasters 12kg × 2

LINCOLN

CAFE
ON SITE

OPEN TO
THE PUBLIC

COFFEE
COURSES

BUY BEANS
ONLINE

BUY BEANS
IN STORE

104 STOKES COFFEE

The Lawn, Union Road, Lincoln, Lincolnshire, LN1 3BU

stokescoffee.com | 01522 523548

f *stokescoffeeroasters* ⊙ *stokescoffeeroasters*

Robert William Stokes founded this legendary Lincoln coffee company more than 120 years ago. Four generations later, his great-grandson Nick Peel is continuing his legacy by producing high-quality speciality coffees and teas for Stokes' own destination cafes (The Lawn, High Bridge, Welton and Stokes To Go) and for wholesale customers across the UK.

It takes a lot for beans to receive the Stokes stamp of approval. The coffees that do are the culmination of the passion, pride and dedication of everyone in the supply chain – from the farmers to Stokes' master roasters who use a wealth of expertise to bring out the best from every bean.

'THE CULMINATION OF THE PASSION, PRIDE AND DEDICATION OF EVERYONE IN THE SUPPLY CHAIN'

With strong ethical and eco principles, Stokes is passionate about making a positive difference and recently partnered with Project Waterfall, a charity that provides clean water in coffee-growing areas. For every bag sold of Jamaican Blue Mountain and Kenyan Burundi, £2 is donated.

Ever evolving, Stokes continues to train the next generation of baristas at its Barista Training Academy. To sample the latest speciality coffees, sign up online to the Stokes Coffee Club to get beans delivered direct to your door.

Established
1902

Roaster make and size
Loring S35
Kestrel 35kg

CAFE ON SITE

OPEN TO THE PUBLIC

OPEN BY INVITE

COFFEE COURSES

BUY BEANS ONLINE

BUY BEANS IN STORE

LINCOLN

105 COURTYARD COFFEE ROASTERS

14d High Street, Eccleshall, Staffordshire, ST21 6BZ

courtyardcoffeeroasters.co.uk | 01785 851024

f courtyardcoffeeroasters

Courtyard Coffee has been in the roasting game since the early 1980s. While its original roaster has been traded in for a newer model (a cherry-red Diedrich 2.5kg infrared drum machine), the company ethos remains the same: to work exclusively with ethical importers and roast the best beans in small batches.

Established
2015

Roaster make and size
Diedrich 2.5kg

'FOUNDER DAVID WIGGINS CREATES A SWEET AND TOASTY MEDIUM CITY-ROAST'

Beans are sourced from Africa, India, Indonesia, Central America and South America for the Courtyard collection of around 20 single-origin arabicas and high-quality blends. Regardless of their country of origin, founder David Wiggins allows the beans to fully develop during roasting to reveal a sweet and toasty medium city-roast.

David is also passionate about crafting a range of decaffeinated beans and there are at least three options available at any time, all of which are water processed.

Beans are available online and on-site, and roastery tours can be booked in advance.

OPEN BY INVITE

COFFEE COURSES

BUY BEANS ONLINE

BUY BEANS IN STORE

106 QUARTER HORSE COFFEE ROASTERS

10 Kenyon Street, Birmingham, B18 6AR

quarterhorsecoffee.com | 01212 745740

f quarterhorsecoffee ⊙ quarterhorsecoffee

It's an exciting time for this much-loved Birmingham roastery. After celebrating its tenth birthday last year, at the start of 2023 Quarter Horse relocated its HQ to a fresh space in the city's Jewellery Quarter.

The new roastery houses an espresso bar where beans usually reserved for the Quarter Horse Coffee Club (a monthly subscription service) are prepared for the coffee curious. Four times larger than the original site, the Jewellery Quarter venue is powered by solar panels and features a fully electric roaster which replaced the old gas model.

Established
2012

Roaster make and size
Giesen W30A 30kg, Stronghold S9X 8kg

'JOIN THE QUALITY CONTROL TEAM FOR A CUPPING SESSION AT THE ROASTERY'

Visit the online shop to take your pick from a varied stable of coffees (including the bestselling house blend Dark Horse Espresso), a seasonally rotating selection of filter coffees and speciality-grade compostable pods.

If you're in town, the OG Bristol Street cafe remains a very reliable choice for great coffee. It features an extended brunch menu too and, in summer, a suntrap terrace that's the perfect place to chill with a cold brew. Visitors can even book to join the quality-control team for a cupping session at the roastery.

CAFE ON SITE

OPEN BY INVITE

COFFEE COURSES

BUY BEANS ONLINE

BUY BEANS IN STORE

NOTTINGHAM
COFFEE
FESTIVAL
BRINGING TOGETHER NOTTINGHAM'S
COFFEE COMMUNITY 21/10/2023
200°
www.nottscoffeefestival.com

107 HUNDRED HOUSE COFFEE

SY8 Studios, Gravel Hill, Ludlow, Shropshire, SY8 1QX

hundredhousecoffee.com

f *hundredhousecoffee* ⊙ *hundredhousecoffee*

A track record of producing outstanding coffees and a reputation for eye-catching packaging have rewarded Hundred House with a stature as one of the Midlands' coffee-roasting heavy hitters.

Founders Matt Wade and Anabelle De Gersigny have extensive experience in the art world, so supporting creativity was a key consideration when they launched the roastery in 2016. Through their Art + Industry programme, they host interactive coffee-event installations, deliver student product-development projects with nearby schools and commission community-led initiatives which celebrate local culture and heritage.

'COFFEE-CURIOUS CONNOISSEURS WILL ENJOY THE FREAK & UNIQUE COLLECTION OF OUT-OF-THE-ORDINARY COFFEES '

Dive into the Hundred House online shop and you'll find the Great Taste award-winning Bon Bon (a sweet and sticky espresso blend) and Nom Nom (a coffee with 50 per cent less caffeine than the average roast).

Curious coffee connoisseurs will enjoy the Freak & Unique collection of out-of-the-ordinary coffees, complete with limited-edition artwork that can be bought to directly support creative initiatives.

Established
2016

Roaster make and size
Diedrich IR-12 12kg,
Probat P12 12kg

OPEN BY INVITE

BUY BEANS ONLINE

LUDLOW

108 METHOD COFFEE ROASTERS

50-51 Cherry Tree Walk, Worcester, Worcestershire, WR1 3BH

methodroastery.com | 01905 780070

f *methodroastery* ⊙ *methodroastery*

One of the core aims of this Worcester roastery is to close the gap between coffee farmer and consumer. By sourcing beans direct and forming long-term relationships with growers, the Method team are able to share the stories behind the coffees they sell and serve at their roastery-cafe.

Sustainability is another important factor for the crew. The business was recently certified carbon neutral, which is testament to the changes they've implemented such as introducing carbon-negative packaging and partnering with carbon-negative coffee farms.

'THE BUSINESS WAS RECENTLY CERTIFIED CARBON NEUTRAL'

If you can't make it to the roastery's railway-arch cafe to sample or buy beans, its catalogue of coffees is also available to order online (both as one-off purchases and subscriptions). The line-up changes frequently, but recent roaster favourites include an exclusive micro-lot from award-winning Colombian producer Café Granja La Esperanza and a specially prepared micro-lot from one of the founders of the Aruca co-operative in Honduras, with whom the team spent time in 2022.

Established
2014

Roaster make and size
Vintage Probat UG22 25kg

CAFE ON SITE

BUY BEANS IN STORE

109 STUDIO COFFEE ROASTERS

Unit 10 Withy Wells Business Park, Spetchley, Worcester, Worcestershire, WR5 1RW

studioroasters.com | 07391 690802

f studioroastersuk ⊙ *studioroasters*

Antipodean coffee fanatic and Studio founder Chris Shadforth has taken in some remarkable vistas on his path through the world of coffee – from the lush forests of the Adelaide Hills in Australia to the manicured gardens of Worcestershire's Spetchley Park Estate.

His work in the industry started in the small town of Hahndorf, 16 miles east of Adelaide, where he rose through the ranks to become a sensory judge in state and national barista competitions. His climb continued when he became head barista trainer for a large roastery in Sydney.

'SKILL UP ON EVERYTHING, FROM BREWING BASICS TO LATTE ART'

It was on returning to the UK in 2021 that Chris decided to set up his own roastery and established Studio in Gloucestershire. Soon a number of local coffee shops were stocking his South American and East African beans, and within a year he'd moved to roomier premises in Worcester to keep up with demand.

Alongside a diverse collection of coffees, Studio offers training courses for baristas of all levels who can skill up on everything from brewing basics to latte art. Tailored sessions are also available for those who want to achieve a specific goal. Book a course in summer and it's likely you'll be treated to an alfresco beer break on Studio's iconic pink sofa.

Established
2021

Roaster make and size
Silon ZR7 7kg

OPEN BY INVITE

COFFEE COURSES

BUY BEANS ONLINE

BUY BEANS IN STORE

● CAFES

● ROASTERIES

Find more good cafes and roasteries on pages 192–199

All locations are approximate

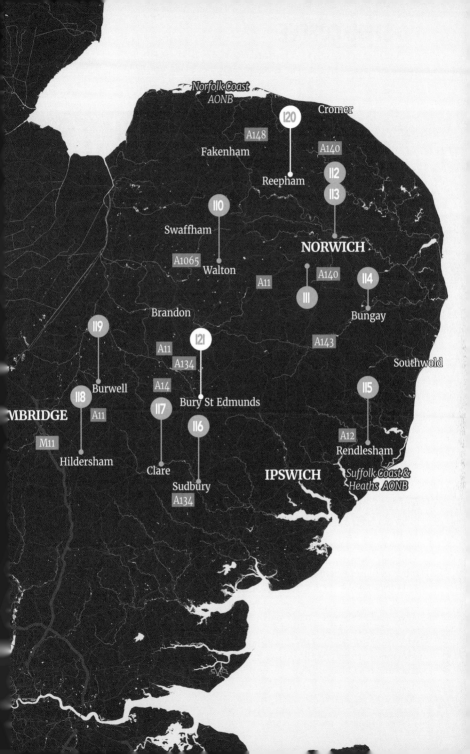

110 SHOU COFFEE

62 High Street, Watton, Thetford, Norfolk, IP25 6AH

07311 674032

f *shoucoffee62* ⊙ *shou.coffee*

On first impressions this Norfolk newbie looks like other contemporary minimalist coffee shops, but spend some time at Shou and you'll discover its individuality is all in the detail.

When brothers Cal and Ed Cheung founded the cafe in November 2022, they brought creative inspiration to the venture from their other interests: the name Shou (roughly translating to 'observe, guard or serve' in Chinese) was inspired by one of tattooist Ed's inkings, while potter Cal crafted the beautiful ceramics in which the coffee and food are served. The brothers' creativity is also reflected in the local artwork adorning the walls.

TIP FEAST ON SANDWICHES PACKED WITH FILLINGS INSPIRED BY ED'S TRAVELS

Rooted in their Norfolk community, Cal and Ed are keen to champion as many local producers as possible, so the house coffee is sourced from Etude in Bungay (a 40-minute drive away) and the retail shelves are crammed with work from local craft-makers and artists.

Shou is currently an espresso-only set-up, but there are plans to add pourover options. The dark chocolate, caramel and berry flavours of the seasonal Prelude blend make it the perfect base for a sublime flat white, while those who prefer citrus notes should check out the Colombia Huila single origin.

Established
2022

Key roaster
Etude Coffee

Brewing method
Espresso

Machine
La Marzocco
Linea Classic

Grinder
Mahlkonig E65S

Opening hours
Tue–Sat
8am–3pm

WATTON

REUSABLES ACCEPTED | BIKE FRIENDLY | DOGS WELCOME | BUY BEANS IN STORE

176

||| CIRCUS HEAD

Wymondham, Norfolk

circushead.co.uk

f circushead *○ circusheadcic*

The worlds of medicine and speciality coffee rarely collide, except at Circus Head where the shots are pulled by an off-duty paramedic who's also a trained barista.

The roaming not-for-profit organisation is run by volunteer ambulance staff and paramedics, with all proceeds from coffee sales going towards wellbeing activities and projects that support medical workers at risk of a mental-health crisis or clinical burnout.

The pop-up coffee shop currently makes appearances at events across Norfolk and Suffolk. However, the team are fundraising for the restoration of a vintage ambulance which will bring their coffee offering, along with first-aid training, to a wider audience.

London roastery The Gentlemen Baristas supplies the beans which are prepared as espresso on a Fracino machine, and as whistle-clean filter brews via V60, Kalita Wave and AeroPress.

TIP CIRCUS HEAD OFFERS FREE CPR AND FIRST-AID TRAINING

Naturally, community is at the core of Circus Head: the organisation is built on a shared belief that engaging with local communities through coffee brings joy and welcome distraction in hard times. Want to play your part? Ask about the Bad Day Button pay-it-forward scheme and stump up for a coffee for someone who really needs it.

Established
2022

Key roaster
The Gentlemen Baristas

Brewing method
Espresso, AeroPress, batch brew, Kalita Wave

Machine
Fracino Contempo 2

Grinder
Nuova Simonelli MDJ, Mahlkonig Guatemala

Opening hours
As per event

REUSABLES ACCEPTED

WIFI

BIKE FRIENDLY

DOGS WELCOME

BUY BEANS IN STORE

COFFEE COURSES

112 FIKA NORWICH

25 Wensum Street, Norwich, Norfolk, NR3 1LA

fikanorwich.co.uk

f *fikanorwich* ⓘ *fikanorwich*

Mark Lawrence describes his inclusive coffee shop on Norwich's Wensum Street as *'a conversational space where you can talk to friends you haven't yet met'*. This convivial vibe extends to breaking down barriers between barista and customer (literally: there is no coffee bar dividing the two).

Mark's seriousness about crafting exceptional caffeine comes with a side order of fun – there's always a can of condensed milk on hand for sweet creations, and espresso is pulled into all manner of carbonated drinks. Follow Fika's Instagram grid for a daily pic of iconic cartoon characters having caffeinated adventures in the cafe.

TIP FIKA FINISHES THE WORKING WEEK WITH BLACK METAL FRIDAYS

The coffee catalogue changes constantly as Mark discovers new beans. Top-tier roasteries such as Plot, Full Court Press and New Ground make regular appearances, and he's also working with Stephen at Lucid in Belfast in the creation of Fika's first collaboration roast.

A small selection of bakes complements the coffee and includes seasonal specials such as mulled apple cake, chocolate-orange truffle brownies and sugar waffles.

Established
2019

Key roaster
Origin Coffee
Roasters

Brewing method
Espresso,
batch brew,
Kalita Wave

Machine
La Marzocco
Linea Classic

Grinder
Mahlkonig EK43 S,
Anfim SP II+

Opening hours
Mon–Fri
8am–2pm

REUSABLES ACCEPTED · WIFI · BIKE FRIENDLY · DOGS WELCOME · BUY BEANS IN STORE · OUTDOOR SEATING

113 THE YARD COFFEE

1a Pivotal House, Orford Yard, Red Lion Street, Norwich, Norfolk, NR1 3TB

theyardcoffee.co.uk | 01603 299034

f *theyardcoffee* ◎ *the_yard_coffee*

Norwich's wilting shoppers head to this stunning light-drenched glass building in the heart of the city to quench their thirst for good coffee. The Yard is a beautiful spot in which to savour a full-bodied, caramel-forward flat white crafted with beans from the city's Symposium Coffee Roasters.

Coffee fans wishing to manifest summery vibes perch in the airy atrium to sip house espresso Agua Santa, paired with a floral chocolate brownie. Those preferring to hide away from the hustle and bustle opt for a cosy nook in The Back Yard where they can explore a drinks list that includes coffee cocktails, natural wine and craft beer.

TIP TO COOL DOWN ON A HOT DAY, YOU CAN'T BEAT AN ICED SPICED CHAI

'We are all about the good vibes,' says co-owner Georgia Gallant. *'Being in the city centre, we want people to see us as an oasis of calm where they can have a break from the rush and enjoy the kind of chill time that a well-crafted cup of coffee brings.'*

Friendly baristas ensure everyone feels welcome, while the unique high-ceilinged, greenhouse-style building creates a pleasing rendezvous spot for all kinds of community events, including book launches, flower arranging workshops and a cocktail club.

Established
2021

Key roaster
Symposium Coffee Roasters

Brewing method
Espresso

Machine
Conti Monte Carlo

Grinder
Anfim SP II

Opening hours
Mon–Sat
8.30am–5pm

WIFI | DOGS WELCOME | OUTDOOR SEATING

114 THE FRONT ROOM

28 Earsham Street, Bungay, Suffolk, NR35 1AQ

thefrontroombungay.co.uk | 01986 948261

f thefrontroombungay ⓞ thefrontroombungay

A mecca for those who worship at the altar of dough, this family-run cafe-bakery in the market town of Bungay proves that it's always better to pair your coffee with something carby than to take it straight up. Few passersby can resist the pull of the day's goodies that call, siren-like, from the shop window – even before the waft of fresh bread and ground coffee lures them through the door.

Once inside, iced cinnamon swirls, creme-pat-infused choux buns and sticky almond cake are just a few of the daily-baked delicacies that persuade visitors to ditch the idea of a simple coffee and instead indulge in a second breakfast or an afternoon pick-me-up. Not that the coffee alone isn't tempting, thanks to a trusty house roast from London's Climpson & Sons and the line-up of guest beans from local roasteries.

TIP GRAB A LOAF AND BAG OF CLIMPSON BEANS FOR TOMORROW'S COFFEE AND TOAST

When lunchtime rolls round, a bill of savoury pastries, soups, salads and filled brioche emerges from the bakery kitchen. It's a mostly takeaway set-up (there are a handful of chairs on the pavement for perching), so don't forget your reusable cup.

Established
2019

Key roaster
Climpson & Sons

Brewing method
Espresso

Machine
La Marzocco
Linea PB

Grinder
Anfim Caimano OD,
Mahlkonig EK43

Opening hours
Mon–Sat
9am–4pm
Sun
10am–2pm

REUSABLES ACCEPTED   **DOGS WELCOME**   **BUY BEANS IN STORE**   **OUTDOOR SEATING**

BUNGAY

180

115 HARVEY & CO

7-9 America House, Base Business Park, Rendlesham, Suffolk, IP12 2TZ

harveyandco.uk | 07904 811481

f harveyandcobread ◎ harvey_andco

If the heady aroma of freshly ground coffee and hand-baked loaves don't lure customers through the door of this Rendlesham coffee shop then the prospect of a "sourdough peepshow" is guaranteed to pique their interest. At Harvey & Co, the bakers let customers in on their sourdough secrets by showcasing their dough-folding and proving prowess.

Curious visitors can spy on the bakers doing their work next door while they enjoy the results of their labours in the form of toasties oozing with mozzarella and garlic aioli, sourdough romana pizzas and crisp buttery croissants.

TIP PERUSE THE COUNTER FOR SPECIALS LIKE SOUR CHERRY AND PISTACHIO BUNS

In 2021, Harvey and Sarah Allen decided to bring "real" baked goods to the local people of rural Suffolk. In just a short space of time the couple, along with head of bread Carl Brennan and a team of bakers, have found themselves supplying indie venues across the county.

The best bit is that anyone can drop by and get a slice of the action. A smooth flat white made from Butterworth & Son's award-winning 4Bean Blend and a flaky almond croissant crafted using top-shelf French butter make for a gratifying midmorning snack. Visitors can also swing by for breakfast, brunch and lunch to experience the pastries, sandwiches, traybakes and other treats in all their carb-laden glory.

Established
2021

Key roaster
Butterworth & Son

Brewing method
Espresso,
batch brew

Machine
La Marzocco KB90

Grinder
Mahlkonig E65S
GbW

Opening hours
Mon-Fri
8am-3pm
Sat
8.30am-2.30pm

REUSABLES ACCEPTED | WIFI | BIKE FRIENDLY | DOGS WELCOME | BUY BEANS IN STORE | OUTDOOR SEATING

116 BISHOPS COFFEE

Unit 1, 101 East Street, Sudbury, Suffolk, CO10 2TP

bishopscoffee.co.uk | 07361 976564

f bishopscoffeesudbury *◎ bishops_coffee*

This may be the only place in Suffolk where you can sip speciality coffee amid a living jungle of greenery. A La Marzocco espresso machine has been incorporated into a houseplant shop so customers can bliss out on just-roasted beans in a tropical paradise where leafy tendrils trail from ceiling to floor.

Founders Lee and Ellie Bishop serve a Rolodex of coffees bronzed at the Bishops micro-roastery. The coffee menu changes depending on what Lee is vibing, but ranges from funky anaerobically fermented Rwandan finds to crowd-pleasing chocolatey Brazilian beans. Guest roasts from the likes of UE and The Gentlemen Baristas also feature.

TIP INDULGENT HOT CHOCS MADE WITH DARK, MILK AND WHITE CHOCOLATE CAN BE PIMPED WITH SYRUPS

A short-but-sweet bill of toasties, panini and bites is available to eat in or take away. Seasonal specials include a roasted squash, stilton and onion panini, vegan all-day breakfast toastie and the rustic pork sausage roll.

Upgrade your home brewing kit with a few choice picks from the retail section. Bags of beans from guest roasteries are also available to take home.

Established
2020

Key roaster
Bishops Coffee

Brewing method
Espresso, filter, Clever Dripper

Machine
La Marzocco

Grinder
Anfim, Ditting

Opening hours
Tue–Sat
8am–4.30pm

WIFI | BIKE FRIENDLY | DOGS WELCOME | BUY BEANS IN STORE | OUTDOOR SEATING

117 SMALLTOWN - CLARE

1 Well Lane, Clare, Suffolk, CO10 8NH

small-t.co.uk

smalltown_bread

Caffeine and carbs are a formidable duo and the popularity of this Clare cafe-bakery is testament to their allure. From early doors, patrons queue at SmallTown's counter to pair silky espresso with lacquered pastries, fruit-bejewelled tarts and chunky slices of chewy sourdough.

The pick of the pack is the cinnamon bun: a neatly knotted twist of homemade dough layered with spicy cinnamon and finished with crystallised sugar. The El Salvadoran house roast from Missing Bean in Oxford – specially selected for its milk chocolate, caramel and hazelnut notes – pairs perfectly with bakes like this, which are delivered daily from SmallTown's sister bakery in Hildersham.

TIP THE GRADE II-LISTED BUILDING IS A LOVELY SPOT TO HUNKER DOWN IN – GRAB A PEW IN THE WINDOW

The array of artisan loaves, buns and cakes on sale were previously crafted at this original site, but such was the demand that the bakery had to move to a bigger space. The new outlet houses a retail space and cafe, which is equally reliable for quality coffee and also offers a guest roast alongside the house espresso.

Established
2020

Key roaster
Missing Bean
Coffee Roasters

Brewing method
Espresso, V60,
batch brew

Machine
La Marzocco

Grinder
Mahlkonig E80

Opening hours
Mon–Sun
8.30am–3.30pm

WIFI · BIKE FRIENDLY · DOGS WELCOME · BUY BEANS IN STORE · COFFEE COURSES · OUTDOOR SEATING

CLARE

183

118 SMALLTOWN - HILDERSHAM

The Artisans, Cooks Pen Farm, Hildersham, Cambridgeshire, CB21 6BS

small-t.co.uk

smalltown_bread

A decade ago it was tricky to track down good coffee in cities, let alone in the countryside, so the existence of this cafe-bakery on a working farm in rural Cambridgeshire is testament to the speciality scene's continuous expansion.

Starting out as a tiny bakery shop serving killer flat whites alongside sourdough loaves and artisan pastries, SmallTown has grown rapidly since it first set down roots in Clare in September 2021. The popularity of the original shop led to this sister site being established to increase the bakery output and create a second cafe for the flourishing following.

TIP LIKE THE GUEST FILTER ROAST? PICK UP A BAG FROM THE RETAIL SHELVES

Make the trip to sink your teeth into a hot-from-the-oven cinnamon knot in a peaceful countryside environment. Coffee from The Missing Bean in Oxford and Wood St in London is on hand to provide the accompanying mellow buzz and is prepared by the team as espresso, batch and V60.

Swing by at lunchtime to make the most of the new midday menu, which marries just-picked organic produce from the farm with SmallTown's homemade breads and goodies.

Established
2022

Key roaster
The Missing Bean

Brewing method
Espresso, V60, batch brew

Machine
La Marzocco

Grinder
Anfim Pratica

Opening hours
Thu-Sun
8.30am-3.30pm

HILDERSHAM

REUSABLES ACCEPTED | WIFI | BIKE FRIENDLY | DOGS WELCOME | BUY BEANS IN STORE | COFFEE COURSES | OUTDOOR SEATING

119 VILLAGE GREEN COFFEE SHOP

105 The Causeway, Burwell, Cambridgeshire, CB25 0DU
villagegreencoffee.com | 01638 741031
f villagegreencoffeeshop ⓘ villagegreen.coffee

This contemporary cafe on the edge of The Fens offers an urban-style coffee experience in a quaint village setting.

From the coffee beans to the cakes, everything is sourced as locally as possible. The Brew Project in Cambridge keeps the cafe's La Marzocco buzzing with a steady supply of Milk Fighter – an espresso blend with notes of creamy cocoa and caramel – and there's also a rotation of single-origin beans available as filter, along with a reliably delish decaf. Carby treats are sourced from the likes of Sapphire Cake Co. and Honest to Goodness Cakes.

TIP THE CAFE IS SUPER FAMILY-FRIENDLY, WITH BOOKS AND TOYS TO KEEP LITTLE ONES ENTERTAINED

Coffee and a slice is the main draw here, but you'll also find a small selection of savouries such as filled croissants, toasties and breakfast sandwiches. Grab a window seat – or an outdoor table in the warmer months – and idle away an hour or two with a flat white and a wedge of something wickedly indulgent.

Short on time? Buy a Village Green KeepCup and get a discount each time you use it.

Established
2017

Key roaster
The Brew Project

Brewing method
Espresso, filter

Machine
La Marzocco
Linea PB

Grinder
Victoria Arduino
Mythos One,
Mahlkonig K30
Vario Air

Opening hours
Tue-Fri
8.30am-4.30pm
Sat
9am-4pm
Sun
10am-2pm

REUSABLES ACCEPTED · WIFI · BIKE FRIENDLY · BUY BEANS IN STORE · OUTDOOR SEATING

BURWELL

185

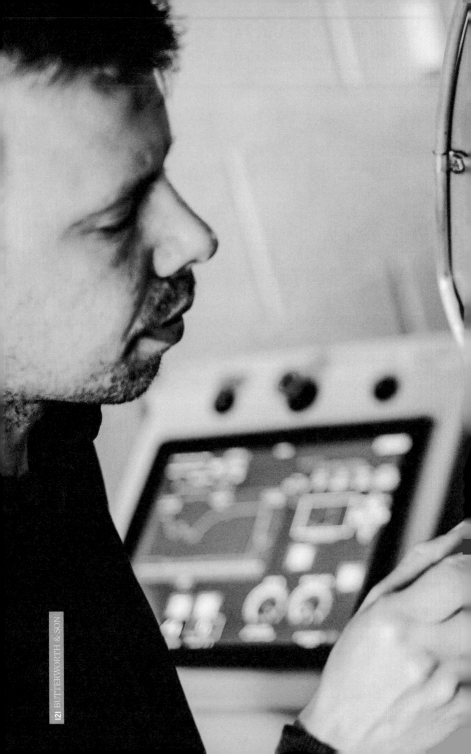

EAST
ANGLIA
ROASTERIES

120 NORFOLK COFFEE CO.

Salle Moor Hall Farm, Wood Dalling Road, Salle, Norwich, Norfolk, NR10 4SB

norfolk.coffee | 01603 872871

f *norfolkcoffeeco* ⊙ *norfolkcoffee*

This Norfolk roastery may be located in a 500-year-old barn in a historic 132-acre estate (once owned by the Boleyn family) but founder Steve Perrett takes a strictly contemporary approach to coffee roasting.

In this rural setting he uses a new Giesen W15A (nicknamed Sally) to precision roast a spectrum of single-origin beans from traceable farms. Steve avoids automation and instead roasts each batch by hand, carefully tracking temperature, air pressure, drum speed and even the effects of the weather.

'STEVE AVOIDS AUTOMATION AND INSTEAD ROASTS EACH BATCH BY HAND'

Accompanying the collection of single origins is house blend 1549, named after the year of Kett's Rebellion when Norfolk peasants rose up against wealthy landowners over land enclosure. The Brazilian/Peruvian mix reveals notes of milk chocolate, caramel, hazelnut and orange.

Steve doesn't claim to be able to change the world through coffee roasting, but he is committed to doing his bit for the environment and has recently purchased an electric van for local deliveries. The roastery is open two days a week for drink-in coffees and retail purchases – check the website for details.

Established
2014

Roaster make and size
Giesen W15A 15kg

CAFE ON SITE   OPEN BY INVITE   BUY BEANS ONLINE   BUY BEANS IN STORE

121 BUTTERWORTH & SON

1d Boldero Road, Moreton Hall Industrial Estate, Bury St Edmunds, Suffolk, IP32 7BS

butterworthandson.co.uk | 01284 767969

f ButterworthandSon © butterworths

The Butterworth family originally made a name for themselves by producing Suffolk Blend, a tea specially formulated for the area's hard water. Then, in 2011, the Butterworths saw the potential for the business to segue into the speciality coffee scene and joined the world of roasting.

Today, the company is one of East Anglia's leading independent coffee roasteries. It supplies beans to cafes, restaurants and businesses, as well as delivering barista training and equipment servicing, repair, sales and rental.

'THE TASTER PACK IS THE PERFECT WAY TO TRY DIFFERENT STYLES AND COUNTRIES OF ORIGIN'

Rob Butterworth (the son in Butterworth & Son) heads up the enterprise, regularly travelling across the coffee-growing belt to source beans direct from producers. The result is a wide selection of micro-lot coffees, which are processed in various ways including honey, natural and washed. The consistent crowd-pleaser is 4Bean, an incredibly smooth espresso blend delivering flavours of fruit, nut and creamy chocolate.

Coffee fans can get a Butterworth & Son fix by buying beans direct from the website. Overwhelmed by the options? The taster pack is the perfect way to try different styles and countries of origin.

Established
2011

Roaster make and size
Diedrich CR23 23kg,
Diedrich IR5 5kg

BUY BEANS ONLINE

EL RUBI
OLOMBIA
EACH, APRICOT, HONEY

WHOLE BEAN

GUJI HIGHLAND
ETHIOPIA
BLUEBERRY JAM, CREAM

WHOLE BEAN

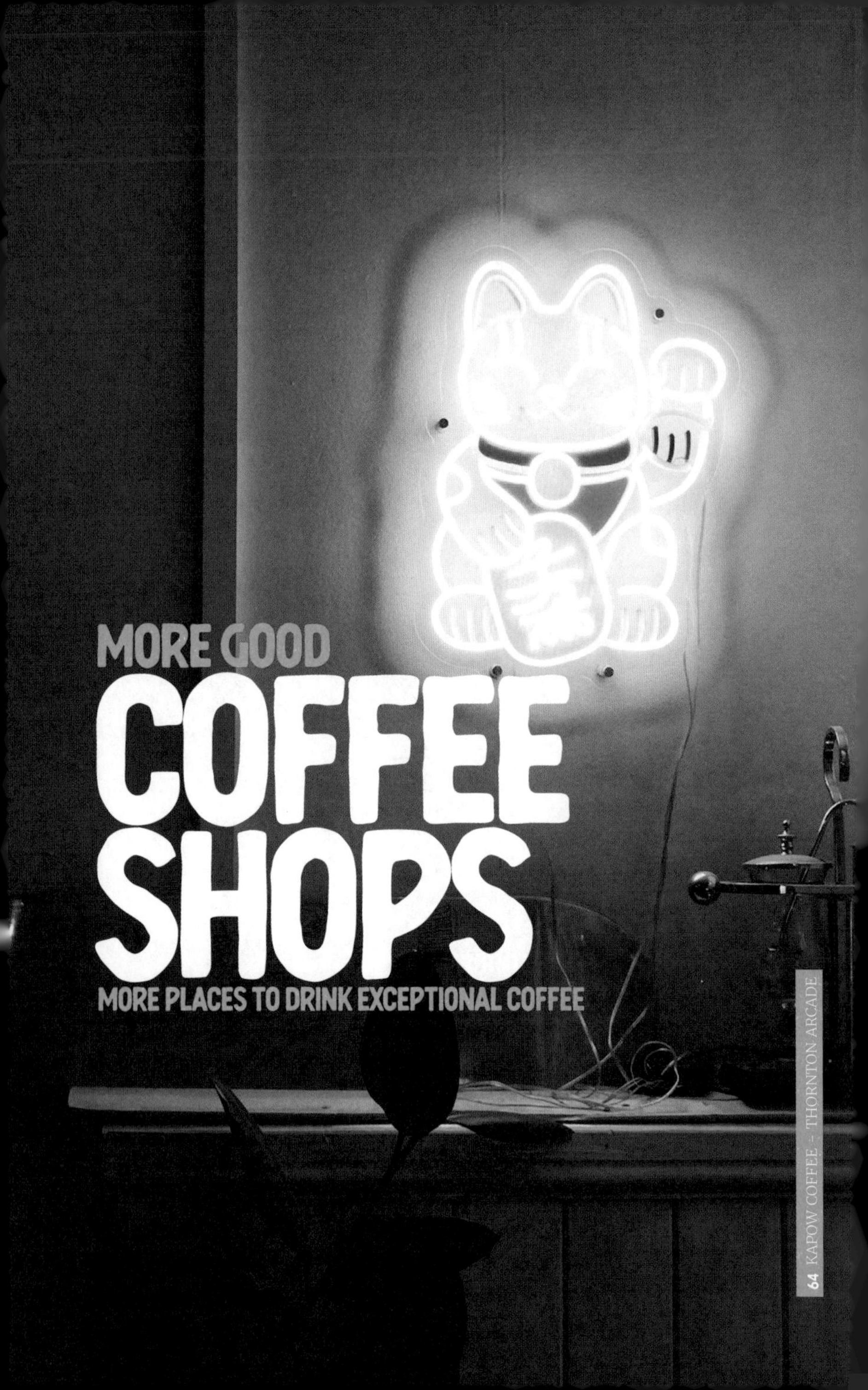

MORE GOOD COFFEE SHOPS

MORE PLACES TO DRINK EXCEPTIONAL COFFEE

64 KAPOW COFFEE – THORNTON ARCADE

122 ALBIE'S COFFEE
22 Snigg Hill, Sheffield,
South Yorkshire, S3 8NB
albiescoffee.co.uk

123 ANCOATS COFFEE CO. - 111 PICCADILLY
111 Picadilly, London Road,
Manchester, M1 2HY
ancoats-coffee.co.uk

124 ANCOATS COFFEE CO. - ROYAL MILLS
Unit 9 Royal Mills, 17 Redhill Street,
Manchester, M4 5BA
ancoats-coffee.co.uk

125 ATRIUM COFFEE
1 St Peter's Square, Manchester, M2 3AE

126 BEAN & LEAF COFFEE HOUSE
67 Hertford Street, Coventry,
West Midlands, CV1 1LB
beanandleafcoffeehouse.co.uk

127 BLEND AT CONTEMPORARY
Weekday Cross, Nottingham, NG1 2GB
blendnottingham.co.uk

128 BLEND AT EAST WEST
Tollhouse Hill, Nottingham, NG1 5FS
blendnottingham.co.uk

129 BLEND AT SNEINTON MARKET
Avenue C, 30 Sneinton Market,
Nottingham, NG1 1DW
blendnottingham.co.uk

130 BLOOMFIELD SQUARE
28-30 Gay Lane, Otley, Leeds,
West Yorkshire, LS21 1BR

131 BOLD STREET COFFEE - THE PLAZA
100 Old Hall Street, Liverpool,
Merseyside, L3 9QJ
boldstreetcoffee.co.uk

132 BOLD STREET COFFEE - LIVERPOOL
89 Bold Street, Liverpool,
Merseyside, L1 4DG
boldstreetcoffee.co.uk

133 BOLD STREET COFFEE - MANCHESTER
53 Cross Street, Manchester, M2 4JN
boldstreetcoffee.co.uk

134 BOLD STREET COFFEE - UNIVERSITY GREEN
Unit 5, 140 Oxford Road,
Manchester, M13 9GP
boldstreetcoffee.co.uk

135 CAFFÈ & CO
8 Dane Court, Rainhill, Prescot,
Merseyside, L35 4LU
caffeandco.com

136 CARTWHEEL COFFEE - BEESTON
1 Stoney Street, Beeston,
Nottingham, NG9 2LA
cartwheelcoffee.com

137 CARTWHEEL COFFEE - NOTTINGHAM
16 Low Pavement, Nottingham, NG1 7DL
cartwheelcoffee.com

138 CEDARWOOD COFFEE COMPANY
10 Winckley Street, Preston,
Lancashire, PR1 2AA
cedarwood.coffee

139 CROSS STREET UNION
Cross Street, Holt, Norfolk, NR25 6HZ

140 FEDERAL CAFE AND BAR - DEANSGATE
194 Deansgate, Manchester, M3 3ND
federalcafe.co.uk

141 FEDERAL CAFE AND BAR - OXFORD ROAD
R3 No2 Circle Square, Oxford Road,
Manchester, M1 7FS
federalcafe.co.uk

142 FLOUR & CO BAKEHOUSE
3 High Street, Eccleshall,
Stafford, ST21 6BW
flourandcobakehouse.co.uk

143 GOOD HONEST BAKERY
631-633 Mansfield Road, Sherwood,
Nottingham, NG5 2FX
goodhonestbakery.co.uk

144 HEIMAT COFFEE ROASTERS
6 Wesley Street, Southport,
Lancashire, PR8 1BN
heimat.coffee

145 HOPEFULLY COFFEE
9-10 Milk Street, Shrewsbury,
Shropshire, SY1 1SZ
hopefullycoffee.com

146 JONAH'S COFFEE
Preston Outdoor Market, Birley Street,
Preston, Lancashire, PR1 2JA
jonahs.coffee

147 KERB KOLLECTIVE
Cambridge Museum of Technology,
Riverside, Cambridge, CB5 8HN

148 KIGALI
2 Stoney Street, Nottingham, NG1 1LG

149 KODA
17 Northway, Scarborough,
North Yorkshire, YO11 1JH
koda-coffee.square.site

150 LAY OF THE LAND
Kings Mill Lane, Sowarth Field Industrial
Estate, Settle, North Yorkshire, BD24 9BS
layoftheland.co.uk

151 LIAR LIAR
2 Albion Hill, Oswestry,
Shropshire, SY11 1QA
liarliarcoffee.co.uk

152 MOW'S COFFEE
151 Arundel Street, Sheffield,
South Yorkshire, S1 2NU
themowbray.co.uk

153 OBSCURE COFFEE
66 Lower Bridge Street, Chester,
Cheshire, CH1 1RU

154 OFF THE GROUND COFFEE
63 Grange Road, Middlesborough,
North Yorkshire, TS1 5AS
offtheground.coffee

155 OLD GEORGE - HERITAGE
Wellington Mills, 70 Plover Road,
Huddersfield, West Yorkshire, HD3 3HR
old-george.co.uk

156 OLD GEORGE - TOWN HALL
Town Hall, Church Street, Barnsley,
South Yorkshire, S70 2TA
old-george.co.uk

157 ONE PERCENT FOREST
42 Allerton Road, Woolton, Liverpool,
Merseyside, L25 7RG
onepercentforest.co.uk

158 OUT OF THE WOODS - GRANARY WHARF
Waterman's Place, Granary Wharf, Leeds,
West Yorkshire, LS1 4GL
outofthewoods.me.uk

159 OUT OF THE WOODS - WATER LANE
113 Water Lane, Leeds,
West Yorkshire, LS11 5WD
outofthewoods.me.uk

160 PILGRIMS COFFEE HOUSE
Marygate, The Holy Island of Lindisfarne,
Northumberland, TD15 2SJ
pilgrimscoffee.com

161 ROOST COFFEE - ESPRESSO BAR
Unit 6 Talbot Yard, Yorkersgate, Malton,
North Yorkshire, YO17 7FT
roostcoffee.co.uk

162 SIPHON - MANCHESTER NORTHERN QUARTER
7 Newton Street, Manchester, M1 1HF
siphonespresso.com

163 SIPHON - RAWTENSTALL
91 Bank Street, Rawtenstall, Rossendale,
East Lancashire, BB4 7QN
siphonespresso.com

164 STOKES HIGH BRIDGE CAFE
207-209 High Street, Lincoln, LN5 7AU
stokescoffee.com

165 STOKES TO GO
210 High Street, Lincoln, LN5 7AU
stokescoffee.com

166 STOKES WELTON CAFE
5a Lincoln Road, Welton,
Lincoln, LN2 3HZ
stokescoffee.com

167 SUFFOLK COFFEE POD
156 Highfield Road, Ipswich,
Suffolk, 1P1 6DJ
suffolkcoffeepod.com

168 THE BOATHOUSE
Newmillerdam Country Park, Wakefield,
West Yorkshire, WF2 6PZ
boathousenewmillerdam.com

169 THE CURIOUS COFFEE
COMPANY - EASINGWOLD
Market Place, Easingwold, York, YO61 3AG
curiouscoffee.co

170 THE CURIOUS COFFEE COMPANY - HAXBY
Unit 8 Haxby Shopping Centre, Haxby,
North Yorkshire,YO32 2LU
curiouscoffee.co

171 THE SEA SHANTY
4 Atherton Street, New Brighton,
Merseyside, CH45 2NY

172 TOAST HOUSE
22 Leeds Road, Ilkley,
West Yorkshire, L29 8DS
toasthouse.co.uk

173 TWO BROTHERS - ALTRINCHAM
53 Stamford New Road, Altrincham,
Cheshire, WA14 1DS
twobrothers.coffee

174 TWO BROTHERS - ST HELENS
The BookStop, 11 Bridge Street, St Helens,
Merseyside, WA10 1NN
twobrothers.coffee

175 TWO BROTHERS - WARRINGTON
Warrington Market, Warrington,
Cheshire, WA1 2NT
twobrothers.coffee

176 VIBE WITH
67 Mansfield Road, Nottingham, NG1 3FN
vibewithcoffee.com

177 WAYLAND'S YARD - BIRMINGHAM
42 Bull Street, Birmingham, B4 6AF
waylandsyard.com

178 WAYLAND'S YARD - WORCESTER
6 Foregate Street, Worcester, WR1 1DB
waylandsyard.com

179 WHARF ST COFFEE
Block A Shipley Wharf, Wharf Street,
Shipley, West Yorkshire, BD17 7DW

180 WYLDE BAKERY
220 Bebington Road, Bebington, Wirral,
Merseyside, CH42 4QF
wyldecoffee.com

181 YOLK.
29 Goose Gate, Hockley,
Nottingham, NG1 1FE
yolknotts.com

MORE GOOD
ROASTERIES
ADDITIONAL PLACES TO SOURCE BEANS FOR YOUR HOME HOPPER

182 200° COFFEE
The 200 Degrees Roast House,
Meadow Lane, Nottingham, NG2 3HE
200degs.com

183 ABE & CO COFFEE
Rear 60, Bury Old Road, Whitefield,
Manchester, M45 6TL
abeandco.co.uk

184 ANCOATS COFFEE CO.
Unit 9 Royal Mills, 17 Redhill Street,
Manchester, M4 5BA
ancoats-coffee.co.uk

185 BARISTOCRACY COFFEE ROASTERS
Unit 2 Larch Court, West Chirton North
Industrial Estate, North Shields, Tyne
and Wear, NE29 8SG
baristocracycoffee.com

186 BLOSSOM COFFEE ROASTERS
16 Longwood Road, Manchester, M17 1PZ
blossomcoffee.co.uk

187 CARTWHEEL COFFEE ROASTERS
Unit S1 Roden House, Roden Street,
Nottingham, NG3 1JH
cartwheelcoffee.com

188 CARVETII
Unit 3c Threlkeld Business Park,
Threlkeld, Cumbria, CA12 4SU
carvetiicoffee.co.uk

189 CRUDE COFFEE ROASTERS
Unit 22 Hillside Business Park, Bury St
Edmonds, Suffolk, IP32 7EA
crudedrinks.co.uk

190 ECHELON COFFEE ROASTERS
Unit 20 Penraevon Industrial
Estate, Penraevon Street, Leeds,
West Yorkshire, LS7 2AW
echeloncoffee.co.uk

191 ETUDE COFFEE
Unit M2 Earsham Mill Estate,
Church Road, Earsham,
Norfolk, NR35 2TQ
etude.coffee

192 FIKA COFFEE ROASTERS
Unit 2b Riverside Industrial Estate,
Langley Park, Durham, DH7 9TT
fikacoffeeroasters.co.uk

193 HARMONY COFFEE
York, North Yorkshire
harmonycoffee.co.uk

194 HASBEAN
Unit 16 Ladford Covert, Ladfordfields
Industrial Estate, Stafford,
Staffordshire, ST18 9QL
hasbean.co.uk

195 HEART AND GRAFT COFFEE ROASTERY
30 Holyoak Street, Manchester, M40 1HB
heartandgraft.co.uk

196 MONKEYBOARD COFFEE
Unit 96 Compass Industrial Park,
Liverpool, Merseyside, L24 1YA
monkeyboardcoffee.co.uk

197 NORTH STAR COFFEE ROASTERS
Unit 10, 280 Tong Road, Leeds,
West Yorkshire, LS12 3BG
northstarroast.com

198 OUTPOST COFFEE ROASTERS
32 Salisbury Square,
Nottingham, NG7 2AB
outpost.coffee

199 PILGRIMS COFFEE
Marygate, The Holy Island of Lindisfarne,
Northumberland, TD15 2SJ
pilgrimscoffee.com

200 POCOESPRESSO
29 The Gables, Cottam, Preston,
Lancashire, PR4 0LB
pocoespresso.com

201 PODDA & WREN COFFEE ROASTERS
4 Elephant Yard, Kendal,
Cumbria, LA9 4QQ
podda-wren.co.uk

202 RED BANK COFFEE ROASTERS
Unit 12 Boundary Bank, Kendal,
Cumbria, LA9 5RR
redbankcoffee.com

203 REVOLUTION COFFEE ROASTERS
Unit 27 New Hall Hey Business Park,
Rossendale, Lancashire, BB4 6HL
revolution-coffee.co.uk

204 RUMOUR COFFEE CO.
Suffolk
rumourcoffee.co.uk

205 SALFORD ROASTERS
Unit E Protector Lamp Business
Park, Lansdowne Road, Eccles,
Manchester, M30 9PH
salfordroasters.co.uk

206 SEAMOOR COFFEE
Bridge Street, Bradwell, Hope Valley,
Derbyshire, S33 9HE
seamoorcoffee.co.uk

207 STEWARTS OF TRENT BRIDGE
Unit 31 Avenue C, Sneinton Market,
Nottingham, NG1 1DW
stewartscoffees.co.uk

208 STRANGERS COFFEE COMPANY
10 Dove Street, Norwich,
Norfolk, NR2 1DE
strangerscoffee.com

209 SYMPOSIUM COFFEE ROASTERS
Unit 21c Hellesdon Park Industrial Estate,
Alston Road, Norwich, Norfolk, NR6 5DS
symposiumcoffee.co.uk

210 THE BREW PROJECT
Byways, Holbrook Road, Ipswich,
Suffolk, IP9 2RU
brewproject.co.uk

211 THE PENNY ROASTER
Holbrook, Ipswich, Suffolk
pennyroaster.com

212 TWO BROTHERS ROASTERY
Warrington Market, 2 Time Square,
Warrington, Cheshire, WA1 2NT
twobrothers.coffee

213 YORK EMPORIUM
Unit 4-5 Rose Avenue, Rose
Centre, York Business Park, York,
North Yorkshire, YO26 6RX
yorkemporium.co.uk

MEET OUR COMMITTEE

The *Independent Coffee Guide England: North, Midlands and East* committee is made up of a small band of leading coffee experts from across the regions, who have worked with Salt Media and the coffee community to oversee the creation of this guide

Dave Olejnik

Having always sought out great coffee shops, it was during Dave's time living in Seattle (where he worked as a touring guitar tech) that he was inspired to fully divert his energy into coffee. He returned to the UK and worked for Coffee Community, travelling the world as a trainer and consultant, before launching Laynes Espresso in Leeds in 2011.

Paul Meikle-Janney

Paul is a founder of Dark Woods Coffee, the multi-award-winning roastery on the outskirts of Huddersfield.

In 1999, Paul started Coffee Community, an international training and consultancy agency for the speciality industry. He's co-written both the City & Guilds and SCA barista qualifications and has been involved in the World Barista Championships and UK Barista Championships since their inception.

Hannah Davies

Hannah's career in the coffee industry has seen her develop from a barista to director of Cup North, an organisation committed to promoting the value of speciality coffee through events.

Since discovering a love for organising coffee events in 2014, Hannah has worked with the UK coffee scene to create festivals, competitions and creative coffee-based content.

David Nickerson-Smith

David was a musician and sound engineer (career highlights include working on *The Basil Brush Show*) before he sidestepped into speciality coffee.

After gaining a couple of years of experience in the industry, in 2020 he opened Quaff East Coffee (with the help of his wife and daughter) in Beccles, East Anglia. He now also works as a regional wholesale manager for London roastery The Gentlemen Baristas.

Ian Steel

Ian's Lancaster coffee roastery, Atkinsons, celebrates its 186th birthday this year.

Ian and his family took over the business in 2005. Despite the roastery's long-established pedigree, Ian continues to be fuelled by the same entrepreneurial and innovative mindset that drives all who work in the speciality coffee sector.

'We need to think like a start-up and to keep pioneering new ideas, no matter how established we are,' says Ian.

Matthew Wade

Matthew trained as a barista and roaster in New Zealand. He brought his coffee experience with him when he returned to London, which led to him playing a leading role in the burgeoning UK coffee scene of the early noughties. Matthew became one of the UK's first Q graders and won several awards for his coffees when he was head roaster at Union Hand-Roasted and Bullet Coffee.

In 2016, Matthew set up Hundred House Coffee, a multi-award-winning roastery in Shropshire.

INDEX

FOR BREW FREAKS, BEAN GEEKS

AND THE SIMPLY CURIOUS ...